The Supported Learning in Physics Project has received major support from

Nuclear Electric

The project is also supported by The Department for Education and Employment

The Open University

LEARNING
IN PHYSICS
PROJECT

PHYSICS OF FLOW

This unit was written by
Chris Butlin and Michael Brimicombe

Heinemann

THE SUPPORTED LEARNING IN PHYSICS PROJECT

Management Group

Elizabeth Whitelegg, Project Director, The Open University

Professor Dick West, National Power Professor of Science Education, The Open University

Christopher Edwards, Project Coordinator, The Open University

Professor Mike Westbrook, Vice-President for Education, Industry and Public Affairs, The Institute of Physics

George Davies, Manager, College Recruitment, Ford of Britain

Geoff Abraham, Project Trialing Manager

Dorrie Giles, Director, Education and Professional Development, Institution of Electrical Engineers

Martin Tims, Manager, Education Programme, Esso UK

Catherine Wilson, Education Manager (Schools and Colleges), Institute of Physics

Production

This unit was written for the Project by Chris Butlin, Science Education Group, The University of York, and Michael Brimicombe, Cedars School, Leighton Buzzard.

Other members of the production team for this unit were:

Elizabeth Whitelegg, Project Director

Christopher Edwards, Project Coordinator and Academic Editor

Andrew Coleman, Editor

John Coleman, Course Assessor

Alison George, Illustrator

Maureen Maybank, Unit Assessor

Julie Lynch, Project Secretary

Sian Lewis, Designer

ISBN 0 435 68842 1

The Institute of Physics, 76 Portland Place, London, W1N 4AA.

First published 1998 by Heinemann Educational Publishers.

© 1998 The Institute of Physics.

Printed in Spain by Edelvives.

For further information on the Supported Learning in Physics Project contact the Information and Marketing Officer, The Centre for Science Education, The Open University, Walton Hall, Milton Keynes, MK7 6AA.

1.1

CONTENTS

The SLIPP units introduce you to a new method of studying – one that you may not have used before. They will provide you with a way of studying on your own, or sometimes in small groups with other students in your class. Your teacher will be available to guide you in your use of this unit – giving you advice and help when they are needed and monitoring your progress – but mainly you will learn about this topic through your own study of this unit and the practical work associated with it.

We expect that you will study the unit during your normal physics lessons and also at other times – during free periods and homework sessions. Your teacher will give you guidance on how much time you need to spend on it. Your study will involve you in a variety of activities – you won't find yourself just reading the text, you will have to do some practical work (which we have called 'Explorations') and answer questions in the text as you go along. (Advice on how long each exploration is likely to take is given.) It is very important that you do answer the questions as you go along, rather than leaving them until you reach the end of a section (or indeed the end of the unit!), as they are there to help you to check whether you have understood the preceding text. If you find that you can't answer a question, then you should go over the relevant bit of text again. Some questions are followed immediately by their answers but you should resist the temptation to read the answer before you have thought about the question. If you find this difficult it may be a good idea to cover up the answer with a piece of paper while you think about the question. Other slightly longer or more demanding questions have their answers at the back of the section. You are likely to need help with these; this might be from a teacher or from working with other students.

It will be up to you to make notes on the physics you have learnt from this unit as you go along. You will need to use these notes to help you revise. You should also keep notes on how you arrived at your answers to the questions in the unit. It is important to show all your working out for each question and to set it out clearly, including the units at every stage. We try to do this in our answers to the questions in this unit.

Most sections start with a short 'Ready to Study' test. You should do this before reading any further to check that you have all the necessary knowledge to start the section. The answers for this test are also at the end of the section. If you have any difficulties with these questions, you should look back through your old GCSE notes to see if they can help you or discuss your difficulties with your teacher, who may decide to go over certain areas with you before you start the section or recommend a textbook that will help you.

The large number of practical explorations in the unit are designed to let you thoroughly immerse yourself in the topic and involve yourself in some real science. It is only after hands-on experiences that you really begin to think about and understand a situation. We suggest that you do some of these explorations with other students who are studying the unit and, when appropriate, present your results to the rest of the class. There are a large number of these explorations and it may not be possible for you to do all of them, so if everyone shares their results with others in the class you will all find out about some of the explorations that you are unable to do.

Your teacher will arrange times when the practical work can be undertaken. For health and safety reasons you must be properly supervised during laboratory sessions and your teacher will be responsible for running these sessions in accordance with your school's or college's normal health and safety procedures.

HEALTH AND SAFETY NOTE

The unit warns you about any potential hazards and suggests precautions whenever risk assessments are required of an employer under the Management of Health and Safety at Work Regulations 1992. We expect that employers will accept these precautions as forming the basis for risk assessments and as equivalent to those they normally advocate for school science. If teachers or technicians have any doubts, they should consult their employers.

However, in providing these warnings and suggestions, we make the assumption that practical work is conducted in a properly equipped and maintained laboratory and that field work takes account of any LEA or school or college guidelines on safe conduct. We also assume that care is taken with normal laboratory operations, such as heating and handling heavy objects, and that good laboratory practice is observed at all times.

Any mains-operated equipment should be properly maintained and the output from signal generators, amplifiers, etc., should not exceed 25 V rms.

One fluid dominates the environment and your life – water. Without it, there is no life. It is the major constituent of blood, which delivers energy to your cells and carries away their poisonous wastes. Blood is pumped around your body by the heart. If that pump fails for a few seconds, your brain ceases to function. A few minutes later, it is damaged beyond recovery. Our lives depend on the ability of our bodies to maintain an adequate flow of blood to all our cells.

However, it is not only in our bodies that fluid flow is of great importance; if you look around, you will find many situations where we depend on fluid flow, for example:

- oil and gas are transported long distances through pipes
- a vast quantity of water flows down pipes in hydroelectric power schemes to convert gravitational energy into electricity
- clean water flows through pipes to our homes
- waste water is carried away in the sewage system
- water flows through heating systems to transfer energy to heat our homes.

In all these situations, the flow has to be controlled – sometimes with great precision, for example in the chemical industry, sometimes with less precision, as in hydroelectric power schemes. And sometimes great care is needed, for example to avoid contamination of drinking water by sewage.

This unit will introduce you to the physics of controlling fluid flow. You will learn how fluids can be moved from one place to another, and how the efficiency of that transport can be calculated.

Some of the many situations where fluid flow is important

We are miserable if we are too hot or too cold. In fact, after breathing, eating and drinking, keeping our surroundings at a comfortable temperature is one of our most vital concerns. It can be a matter of life or death.

Two fluids are used widely in homes to transfer energy from central heating boilers to the living spaces. They are air and water. By controlling the flow of the heating fluid through the rooms, their temperature can be adjusted. As you will see, there are several methods employed to control the flow of fluids, each with its own purpose. Central heating systems are a useful starting-point for our study of fluid flow – they use all of the standard control techniques and they are familiar and easily accessible. So, by looking closely at central heating we can find out about the main concepts and techniques used in controlling fluid flow.

READY TO STUDY TEST

Before you begin this section you should be able to:

- state and use the relationship between pressure, force and area
- describe and explain the properties of fluids, using the kinetic theory of matter
- explain why liquids are essentially incompressible whereas gases are not.
- state and use the relationship between work, force and distance
- state and use the relationship between density, mass and volume
- state and use the relationship between the current in a circuit and its total resistance
- state and use the relationship between power, current and voltage
- state and use the relationship between power, energy and time
- explain what is meant by specific heat capacity.

QUESTIONS

R1 Atmospheric pressure is 100 kPa. A sheet of A4 paper (21 cm × 30 cm) is placed on the ground. Calculate the force of the atmosphere on the top surface of the sheet.

R2 Describe and explain the major physical properties of fluids (both liquids and gases).

R3 A car requires a force of 500 N to move at a steady speed of 10 m s^{-1}. How much work has to be done to keep the car moving at 10 m s^{-1} for a minute?

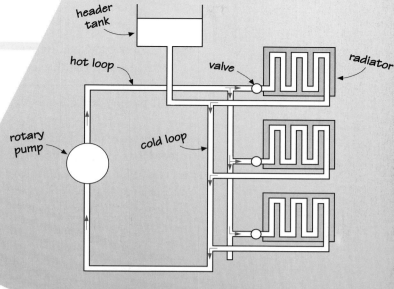

R4 What is the power of a pump that draws a current of 5A when operating at 240V a.c.?

R5 A 10 Ω resistor and a 20 Ω resistor are in series with a 12 V battery. Calculate the rate at which the 10 Ω resistor transfers energy.

R6 Water has a specific heat capacity of 4.2 kJ kg^{-1} K^{-1}. If 5 kg of water cools from 60°C to 20°C, how much thermal energy does it lose?

R7 What is the density of a fluid that has a mass of 1500 kg for every 1 m^3?

R8 How much energy is transfered when this pump operates for 3 minutes?

Figure 2.1
A domestic
heating system

2.1 From boiler to warm room

Figure 2.1 is a schematic diagram of a typical domestic gas-fired hot water heating system. Hot water from the boiler is forced to move through the pipes by a **rotary pump**. Pumps often have a number of possible speeds, so their setting can be used to control the rate at which the hot water moves around the system. **Valves** control the rate at which the hot water flows through each radiator. Notice how the radiators are connected in parallel with each other so that the hot water can flow through them independently. A radiator is designed to allow the rapid transfer of energy from the hot water to the air in the room. It does this by having a large, vertical surface area, often with fins. This allows convection currents to flow past the radiator, picking up energy from its surface and carrying it around the room. Despite its name, only a small proportion of the energy transferred from a radiator is in the form of radiation!

Q1 A typical panel radiator has a maximum output power of 2.0 kW. If the water enters at 60°C and leaves at 40°C, show that 2.4×10^{-2} kg has to enter the radiator in each second. Assume that the specific heat capacity of water is 4.2 kJ kg^{-1} K^{-1}. ◆

The pump in a central heating system maintains the water in the hot loop at a higher pressure than the water in the cold loop. It is this pressure difference (or pressure gradient) that forces the water to flow through each radiator when its valve is opened.

How would you expect the flow rate through a pipe to change as the pressure at the low-pressure end was increased?

It would decrease as the pressure difference would be reduced.

The *flow rate* of a fluid can be stated in one of three ways. These are the **mass flow rate**, the **volume flow rate** and the **fluid speed**. It is easy to get confused between them! The mass flow rate is the mass of fluid entering (or leaving) part of the system in one second. For example, suppose 30 kg of water gushes out of the end of a pipe in a minute. Then the mass flow rate is given by:

$$\text{mass flow rate} = \frac{\text{mass of fluid}}{\text{time}}$$

$$= \frac{30\,\text{kg}}{60\,\text{s}}$$

$$= 0.5\,\text{kg s}^{-1}$$

The volume flow rate is important because it is often the easiest flow rate to measure. (For liquids you need only a measuring cylinder and a stopwatch.) It can be converted, if required, to the mass flow rate if you know the density of the fluid.

 Water has a density of 1000 kg m^{-3}. Can you show that a volume flow rate of 720 litres per hour is the same as a mass flow rate of 0.2 kg s^{-1}?

$$\rho = 1000\,\text{kg m}^{-3}$$

$$V = 720\,\text{litres}$$

$$= 720 \times 10^{-3}\,\text{m}^3$$

$$m = \rho V$$

$$= 1000\,\text{kg m}^{-3} \times 720 \times 10^{-3}\,\text{m}^3$$

$$= 720\,\text{kg}$$

$$t = 1\,\text{hour}$$

$$= 3600\,\text{s}$$

Therefore

$$\frac{\Delta m}{\Delta t} = \frac{720\,\text{kg}}{3600\,\text{s}}$$

$$= 0.2\,\text{kg s}^{-1}$$

The average speed of the fluid is related to the volume flow rate by the cross-sectional area of the pipe that the fluid is going through. Take a look at Figure 2.2. Imagine that all of the fluid is moving at the same speed v. Then all of the fluid in the pipe that is less than a distance $v \times 1$ s from the end will leave the pipe in the next second. The volume V of that fluid is $v \times A \times 1$ s, where A is the cross-sectional area of the pipe. So, the volume flow rate $\dfrac{\Delta V}{\Delta t}$ is given by the equation

$$\frac{\Delta V}{\Delta t} = vA$$

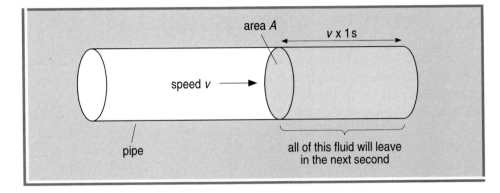

Figure 2.2
Fluid about to leave a pipe

Q2 Air with a density of 1.2 kg m^{-3} is pumped down a duct with a cross-sectional area of 0.60 m^2. If the average speed of the air is 5.0 m s^{-1}, calculate the volume flow rate and mass flow rate down the duct. ◆

Q3 The internal diameter of the copper pipe taking water to and from a radiator is typically 13 mm. If 2.5×10^{-3} kg of water passes through the pipe per second, show that its average speed is about 0.02 m s^{-1}. The density of water is 1.0×10^3 kg m^{-3}. ◆

2.2 Keeping the right temperature

Figure 2.3 overleaf shows a typical electrical central heating pump in a circuit with two switches connected in series with it. The first switch is a timer – it connects the pump to the mains electricity supply at the times programmed into the timer by the householder. The second switch is a **thermostat**. This is often based on a **bimetallic strip**, and is placed at a convenient place somewhere in the house. It closes only when the temperature falls below the preset value. So the pump raises the pressure of the water in the hot loop only if the temperature in the house is too low and the timer has switched on the mains supply. The presence of the thermostat introduces a **negative feedback** loop – it is this that stabilizes the temperature of the house at a comfortable level.

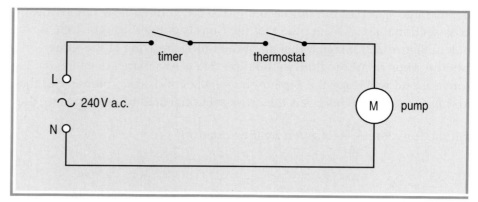

Figure 2.3
A control circuit for a domestic heating system

2.3 Room-by-room control

A thermostat

In practice, a heating system with a single thermostat, like the one shown in Figure 2.3, ends up simply keeping the temperature of the thermostat more or less constant. This does not mean that each room in the house is at a constant temperature. Each room cools by transferring energy to the environment at a different rate. Although the area of radiator surface in the room is chosen to take account of this, by selecting the correct size of radiator, the matching is only approximate. Also, the central heating system is not the only source of heating in most rooms. The rate of cooling will also depend on the number of lights and other electric appliances that happen to be on, the weather conditions at the time and the number of people or animals in the room. So most rooms will be either hotter or colder than the room that contains the thermostat.

It is possible to control the temperature of each room relative to the thermostat by adjusting the valves at the inlet to each radiator. As you can see from Figure 2.4, when the top of the valve is turned, the size of the gap through which the water flows is changed. As the gap gets smaller, the flow rate decreases, transferring energy to the radiator at a lower rate. In this way, by a process of trial-and-error, the output power of each radiator can be matched to the rate at which its room cools through transferring energy to the environment. So the temperature of each room can be set above, below or the same as that of the room that contains the thermostat.

 Why is this method of controlling our central heating not very satisfactory?

The conditions within a room frequently change: electrical equipment is turned on or off; windows and doors may be opened or closed; the sun may come out or there may a brief shower; people and pets may come and go. This means that we would have to repeatedly alter the valves to maintain the desired temperature. Another problem is that many radiator valves leak when they are adjusted after having been left for some time.

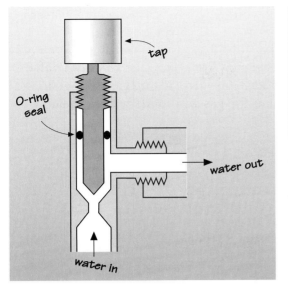

A thermostatically controlled radiator valve

Figure 2.4
A radiator valve

A sensible solution to these problems is to fit thermostatically controlled valves to the radiators. These automatically respond to the surrounding temperature to control the flow of hot water through the radiators.

2.4 The hot water system

Within a water-based central heating system, we need one part of the system to warm the rooms and a separate part keep the water for the hot taps at a constant temperature. One possible system for hot water supply is shown in Figure 2.5.

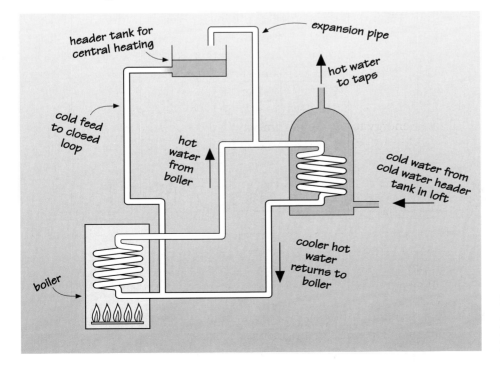

Figure 2.5
A system for heating water for hot taps

Look at Figure 2.6 – what do you think happens when the water is too cold?

The thermostat in the water switches, connecting the **solenoid valve** to the mains supply. This opens the valve, letting gas through to the burners. The pilot light ignites the gas and so the water is heated.

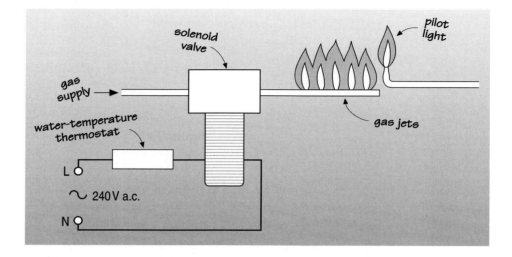

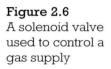

Figure 2.6
A solenoid valve used to control a gas supply

The inner workings of a solenoid valve are shown in Figure 2.7. When there is no charge flowing in the coil, the spring forces the iron slug out of the coil, closing the valve. The solenoid becomes magnetized when it carries a current; it then pulls the iron slug into it. This allows the gas pressure to lift the rubber diaphragm and open the valve. Valves of this type are designed to be 'fail-safe' – if, for any reason, the electricity supply fails, the valve will close automatically.

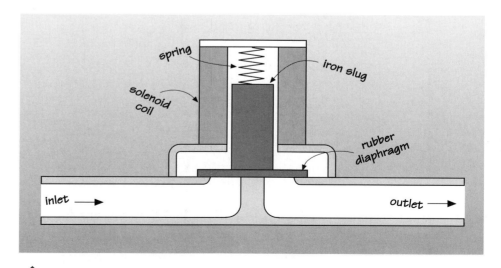

Figure 2.7
A solenoid valve

 What would happen to the central heating system if the gas supply valve was left open in a power cut?

The hot water would boil. This might prove dangerous, although the presence of an overflow pipe to the header tank would prevent the build-up of a dangerously high pressure in the pipes (look back at Figure 2.5).

A solenoid valve is also used to provide a fail-safe for the pilot light; this is shown in Figure 2.8. One junction of a **thermocouple** is heated by the pilot light. This generates enough current to operate a solenoid valve, which allows gas through to the jet.

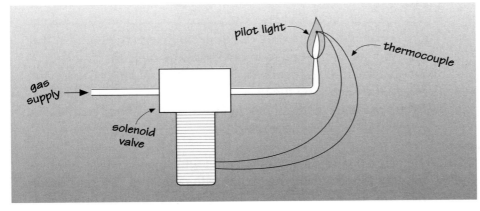

Figure 2.8
The pilot light

 What happens if the pilot light is blown out?

After a short while, the thermocouple fails to generate enough current to keep the solenoid valve open. So the gas supply to the jet is cut off, preventing a continuous flow of unburnt gas into the house.

2.5 Pushing fluids along

If we are to understand more about systems that involve fluid flow, we need to consider the forces involved and the physical details of pipes used.

Imagine that you are a dentist. You need to give a patient a pain-killing injection. So you fill a hypodermic syringe with a local anaesthetic. Now, to make the pain-killer flow through the hole down the centre of the needle, you push the piston and out comes the liquid.

 What are you doing to the pressure of the liquid in the cylinder when you push the piston?

Increasing it.

What is the pressure of the liquid as it escapes from the open end of the needle?

Atmospheric pressure.

Q4 The piston of a hypodermic syringe has a diameter of 2.5 cm. If the force exerted on the liquid is 5.0 N, show that the pressure at one end of the needle is 10 kPa higher than at the other end. ◆

 Why does the liquid stop squirting out of the needle when you stop pressing the piston?

There is no longer a pressure difference between the liquid at the piston and that at the end of the needle providing a force to overcome friction. So friction stops the liquid moving. The friction is between the liquid and the needle. There may even be friction between particles of liquid moving relative to each other; some bits may move faster than other bits.

Friction between the fluid and its container will always transfer some of the input fluid's kinetic energy to heat the fluid and the syringe. So, for a fluid to flow at a steady speed, there has to be a continuous transfer of energy. For our syringe, that energy comes from the source of the pressure difference that is making the fluid flow.

For any liquid to move through a pipe, there needs to be a pressure difference (or pressure gradient). Look at Figure 2.9 – it shows a pipe full of a liquid that is moving from left to right. The pressure at the left-hand end of the pipe is P. At the other end it is $P - \Delta P$.

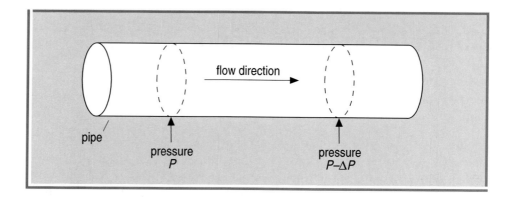

Figure 2.9
A pipe, fluid and pressures

Now let's consider the forces acting on the shaded section of liquid in Figure 2.10. If we neglect gravity and friction, only two forces act, in opposite directions.

 How big is the resultant force on the section of liquid?

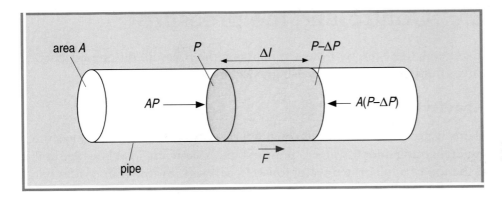

Figure 2.10
The forces acting on a liquid in a pipe

The force on the left-hand end is AP.

The force on the right-hand end is $A(P - \Delta P)$.

So the resultant force is

$$F = AP - A\left(P - \Delta P\right)$$
$$= AP - AP + A\Delta P$$
$$= +A\Delta P$$

Suppose that this force moves the liquid a distance Δl to the right. Since a force has moved along its line of action, some work ΔE will be done.

 How much work?

$$\Delta E = \text{force} \times \text{distance} = (A\Delta P)\Delta l = A\Delta l\, \Delta P$$

Now, as the liquid moved to the right, some liquid was forced out of the end of the pipe. (Think of squeezing toothpaste out of a tube.) The volume V of that liquid is $A\Delta l$. So the work done in forcing a volume V of the liquid just out of the end of the pipe is given by the following formula.

$$\Delta E = V\Delta P \tag{2.1}$$

where ΔE is the work done (J), V is the volume of liquid transferred (m^3), and ΔP is the pressure drop across the pipe (Pa).

Q5 If the pressure drop across the hypodermic needle is 10 kPa, calculate the energy required to squeeze 25 cm^3 of liquid through it. ◆

2.6 Controlling the pressure

In general, there are two ways to maintain the pressure difference that forces fluids to flow: we can use gravity or we can use pumps.

Gravity

Mains water pressure is often provided by gravity. Figure 2.11 shows the general arrangement. Water is pumped into a large enclosed header tank at the top of a hill or in a water tower (a sensor turns the pump off when the tank is full). The pressure of the water behind a domestic tap is then fixed by its vertical distance below the surface of the water in the tank. In general, the tank is mounted high above the taps it feeds.

Figure 2.11
A header tank

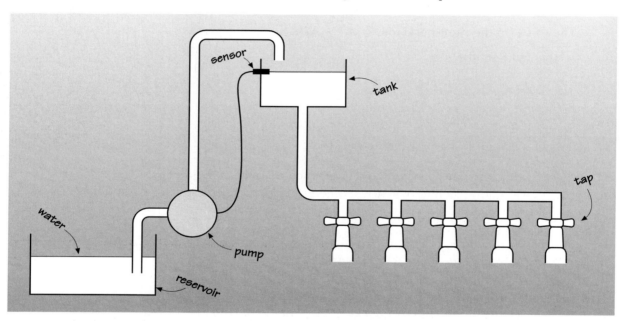

The advantage of this arrangement is that a large number of taps can be fed from one tank. Each tap then has the same pressure, regardless of how many others are open. (Though you may have noticed a change in the flow rate if you have been in a shower when someone else in the house has turned on another tap!)

Header tanks are also used in our homes to maintain the pressure in the hot water system.

Q6 The top surface of the water in the header tank in a two-storey house is 5.0 m above the taps on the ground floor. Calculate the increase in the pressure of water in those taps due to the header tank. (The density of water is 1.0×10^3 kg m^{-3} and $g = 9.8$ N kg^{-1}.) ◆

A water tower that supplies water to homes

Our waste water systems also depend on gravity –
liquids flow down channels such as gutters and sewers
because one end of the channel is higher than the
other. Water flows downhill!

Pumps

The other way to maintain a pressure
difference is to use pumps. **Centrifugal
pumps** are commonly used to pump water.
The liquid is fed in to the centre of a
spinning chamber. As the liquid rotates, it
moves to the outside of the chamber and
its pressure increases. This increased
pressure causes the water to flow.
(See Figure 2.12.)

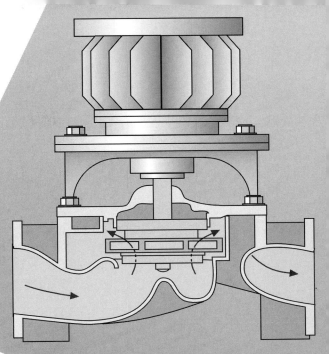

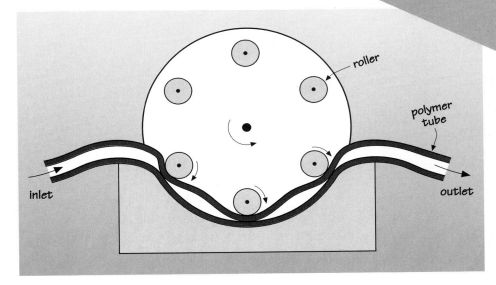

Figure 2.12
A centrifugal pump

Figure 2.13
A peristaltic pump

Peristaltic pumps, like the one shown in Figure 2.13, are used when a
fluid must not be contaminated by the pump. The fluid is contained in a
clear flexible polymer tube that passes under a set of rollers. As these
rollers move over the tube, they push parcels of the liquid from one end
to the other.

Peristaltic pumps are the natural choice for handling blood and other
biological liquids as they are simple, they can manage the flow rates
required and there is no risk of them introducing infection.

Gases are usually pumped with a **compressor**. The sequence illustrated
in Figure 2.14 overleaf shows how a compressor works. Each stroke of
the piston reduces the volume of some gas, which increases its pressure.

To control the pressure of the fluid leaving a pump we can either adjust
the speed of the pump or use a **throttle valve**.

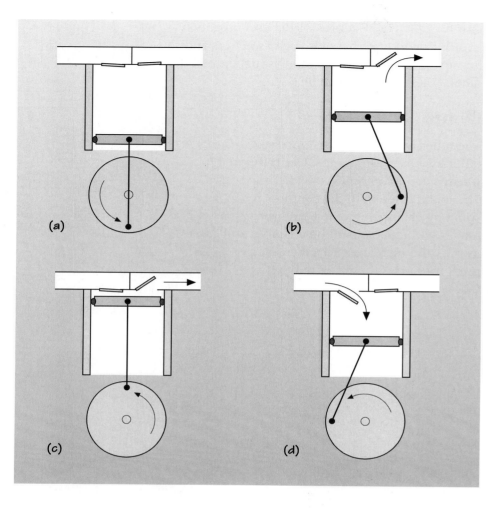

Figure 2.14
How a compressor works

(a)

(b)

(c)

(d)

There are several ways of controlling pump speed. The simplest would be to add a series resistance to the pump, using either a variable resistor (Figure 2.15) or a number of fixed resistors (Figure 2.16). However, using a series resistance not a good choice for controlling pump speed.

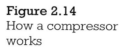 Why do you think using a series resistance is not a good choice?

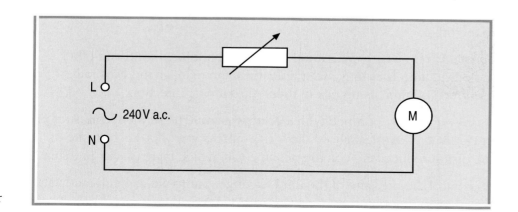

Figure 2.15
A variable resistor

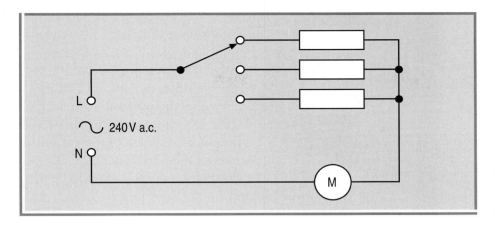

Figure 2.16
Using several fixed
resistors

Although it works, by reducing the current through the pump, a lot
of energy is wasted through heating the resistors.

For pumps that operate from a.c. supplies, and where energy efficiency is
important, control can be provided by **triacs** (which are solid-state
switches that are triggered by pulses). Figure 2.17 shows how a triac is
used. By varying the time at which the pulses are delivered to the triac,
the power delivered to the pump can be varied smoothly from zero to its
maximum value.

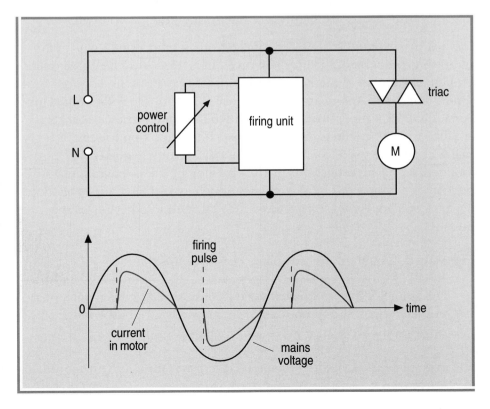

Figure 2.17
Using a triac to
control a pump

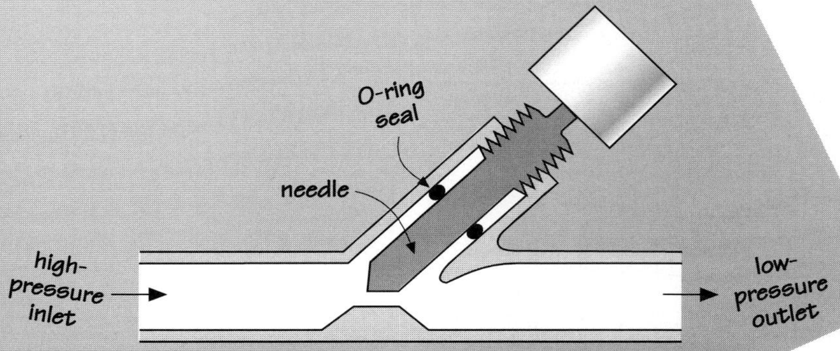

Figure 2.18
A throttle valve

Throttle valves are often inserted in pipes to reduce the pressure of the fluid flowing past them. A typical design is shown in Figure 2.18. As the needle is moved towards its seating, the pressure drop across the valve increases. So for a fixed pressure upstream of the valve, adjustment of the needle position allows the pressure downstream of the valve to be set to any lower value.

O-ring seal

needle

high-pressure inlet

low-pressure outlet

2.7 Using magnetism to measure flow rates

As we have to pay for the gas that we use, gas companies need an accurate and reliable way of measuring our consumption – the gas meter. All buildings that are connected to the gas mains will have a meter. The smallest graduations on domestic meters are tenths of a cubic foot, or 2.8×10^{-3} m^3 (2.8 litres). Gas meters are designed so that they do not require a power supply, so they are not affected by electricity failure.

If you have studied the SLIPP unit *Physics Phones Home*, you will have met up with the idea of **electromagnetic induction**, and you may have come across it and the **Hall effect** in your earlier science course. Both are put to use in various methods of measuring flow, as you will see.

The history behind the discovery of electromagnetic induction is quite interesting and a bit of luck was involved in its discovery being credited to Michael Faraday of the Royal Institution of Great Britain, London, rather than to the American Joseph Henry (1797–1878). Following Hans Oersted's (1777–1851) observation in 1820 that an electric current can produce magnetic effects, many scientists began looking to see if a magnet could be used to produce an electric current. Faraday commenced his investigations in 1824 by moving a bar magnet into a loop of wire connected to an ammeter, much as you have probably done a year or so ago. He was unsuccessful and turned to other researches until 1831.

? Why do you think he was unsuccessful at this time?

His ammeter may not have been sensitive enough, his magnet may not have been strong enough or he may not have had enough turns of wire on his coil.

However, in 1831 he made the famous discovery, though with the aid of an electromagnet. His comments on this were:

Two hundred and three feet [62 m] of copper wire in one length were coiled around a large block of wood; another 203 feet of similar wire were interposed as a spiral between the turns of the first coil, and metallic contact everywhere was prevented by twine. One of these helices was connected with a galvanometer, and the other with a battery of 100 pairs of plates 4 inches [10 cm] square …

When contact was made, there was a sudden and very slight effect at the galvanometer, and there was also a similar effect when the contact with the battery was broken. But whilst the voltaic current was continuing to pass through the one helix no galvanometrical appearances nor any effect like induction upon the other helix could be perceived, although the active power of the battery was proved to be great …

Repetition of the experiments with a battery of 120 pairs of plates produced no other effects; but it was ascertained, both at this and the former time, that the slight deflection of the needle occurring at the moment of completing the connection, was always in one direction, and that the equally slight deflection, produced when the contact was broken, was in the other direction.

MICHAEL FARADAY (1791–1867)

Michael Faraday is considered by many to have been the greatest of all experimental physicists. While many scientists have had their best ideas by the age of 30 he was at his best in his forties, perhaps because he began his education late. His father was a blacksmith and at 13 Michael became a bookseller's errand boy. He learned book-binding, read some of the books and was entranced by an article on elasticity in an encyclopedia and by Mrs Marcet's *Chemistry*. As a result he soon joined a club of people who met weekly to learn elementary science.

His big break came when he was given tickets to attend Sir Humphry Davy's last course of lectures at the Royal Institution. He made very neat notes of these, bound them and sent them to Davy with a letter applying for a job with him. Davy was impressed with the book-binding and recommended he continued with that. However, as he had injured an eye making NCl_3 he took Faraday on as a temporary helper. A few weeks later he gave him a permanent job as an assistant. Faraday later became his coworker and then succeeded him at the Royal Institution.

Davy took Faraday on his grand European tour as helper and valet. This allowed Faraday to meet most of Europe's leading scientists over the one and a half years away. They needed special permission to go because of the Anglo-French war.

During the 1830s, he concentrated on studying electricity, greatly developing this subject. He formed the fundamental laws of electrolysis, discovered electromagnetic induction and used his idea of lines of field producing a strain in materials. This allowed him to make motors, a transformer and a dynamo. Because of his work, people moved away from the old ideas of electricity as a fluid: his was a better theory that explained much more. Although he became a skilful physical and chemical scientist, Faraday always felt that he had a shortcoming in maths.

In some ways Michael Faraday was full of contradictions. He had a great personality, but no social life after 1830. He had great influence on later physicists, but no students. He had highly abstract ideas in science, but was an extremely effective communicator. His Christmas lectures began in 1876 and continue today. We also remember him in the unit of capacitance: the farad.

You might well have conducted a similar experiment in your earlier years with two coils wound round a C-core. One coil would have been connected to a battery and the other to a galvanometer – a sensitive voltmeter.

 When did you see a movement of the galvanometer needle?

Only when the battery connection was made or broken, not while it remained connected.

This same effect had in fact been discovered in America by Joseph Henry the year previously. However, he had a heavy teaching load at Albany Academy, where he worked, and so had delayed publishing his findings. Faraday announced his discovery first and so is credited for it.

We can now develop an explanatory model to help us understand why this phenomenon occurs.

Magnetic flux

If you have used the SLIPP units *Physics, Jazz and Pop* and *Physics Phones Home* you will be familiar with the idea that charges moving (current I) a distance l in a magnetic field experience a force F, where

$F \propto Il$

To turn this into an equation we can introduce a constant of proportionality, which is known as **magnetic flux density, B**, whose unit is the tesla (T). This gives the relationship

$F = BIl$

We can think of a magnetic field as being made up of lines of force, just like an electric field. The more densely packed these lines of force, the stronger the field. We can now think of the magnetic flux density as being the number of lines passing through each square metre of space perpendicular to the lines.

There is another quantity that we use when considering magnetic fields – magnetic flux, ϕ, whose unit is the weber (Wb). This can be visualized as the actual number of magnetic field lines passing through a particular area A that is perpendicular to the field (see Figure 2.19).

The relationship between B and ϕ is

$$B = \frac{\phi}{A} \qquad (2.2)$$

 What unit for magnetic flux density is suggested by Equation (2.2)

The weber per square metre (Wb m^{-2}), so 1 tesla is the same as 1 weber per square metre.

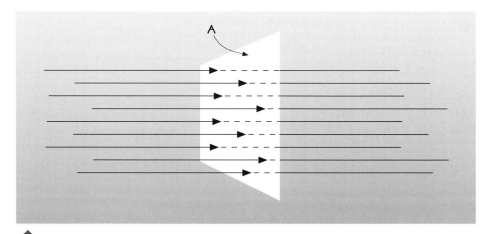

Figure 2.19
Flux at 90° to area *A*

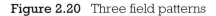 Which of the magnetic fields in Figure 2.20 is uniform?

(a) and (b) only, as only they have flux lines that are parallel to each other.

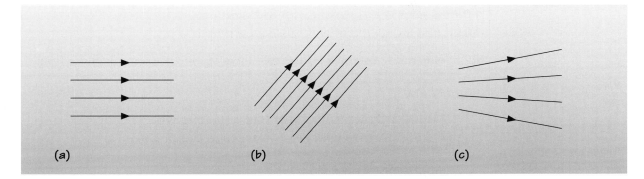

Figure 2.20   Three field patterns

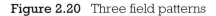 In which part, A, B or C, of the magnetic field in Figure 2.21 is the magnetic flux density strongest?

At A, where the flux lines are closest together.

So, a large number of lines of magnetic flux passing at right angles through a given area would represent a large magnetic flux density. The lines themselves are then considered to be a measure of magnetic flux. The word flux suggests flow, and it may be that Faraday thought in terms of something flowing like water through space. Although nothing does actually flow, physicists do talk of flux 'entering', 'passing through' and 'leaving', as if it really did flow.

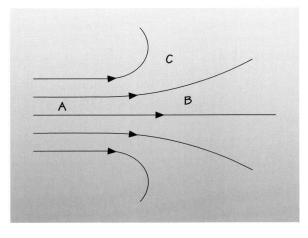

Figure 2.21
Magnetic field pattern

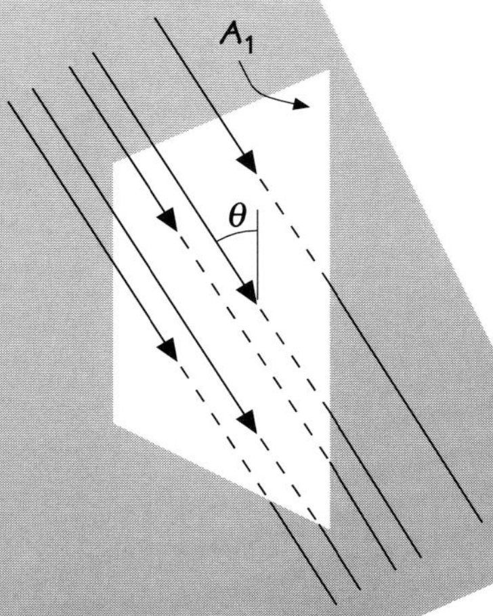

Figure 2.22
Flux at angle θ to area A_1

? A flux passes through an area A_1, which is inclined at an angle θ to the magnetic flux (see Figure 2.22). Write an expression for the area at 90° to the flux.

It is $A_1 \sin\theta$.

? What is the magnetic flux density through area A_1?

$$B = \frac{\phi}{A_1 \sin\theta}$$

Now we are familiar with the fact that currents in magnetic fields experience force, we can look at another aspect of the interaction between charges and magnetic fields. A charge in a changing magnetic field experiences a force. If the charge is in a conductor, this force will be an electromotive force (emf) and will produce the same effects as introducing a battery. If the wire does not form a circuit, a potential difference appears across it – an **induced emf**. If there is a complete circuit, the induced emf will cause a current to flow.

Michael Faraday established the two laws of electromagnetic induction:

First law

When the magnetic flux threading or linking with a circuit is changing, an emf (voltage) is induced in the circuit.

Second law

The magnitude of an induced emf is proportional to the rate of change of flux linkage:

$$E \propto \frac{d(N\phi)}{dt}$$

or

$$E = \text{constant} \times \frac{d(N\phi)}{dt}$$

where E is the emf.

THE TWO LAWS OF ELECTROMAGNETIC INDUCTION

First law

When the magnetic flux threading or linking with a circuit is changing, an emf (voltage) is induced in the circuit.

Second law

The magnitude of an induced emf is proportional to the rate of change of flux linkage:

$E \propto d(N\phi)/dt$

or

$E = \text{constant} \times d(N\phi)/dt$

where E is the emf.

By careful definition of a magnetic flux of 1 weber as that which induces an emf of 1 volt in a 1 turn coil when reduced to zero in 1 second, we can eliminate the constant of proportionality:

$$1 \text{ volt} = \frac{1 \text{ turn} \times 1 \text{ weber}}{1 \text{ second}}$$

The second law of electromagnetic induction is often written in the form of Neumann's equation:

$$E = -N\frac{\mathrm{d}\phi}{\mathrm{d}t}$$

The negative sign indicates that the emf is induced in such a direction that, if the circuit was closed and a current could flow, it would flow so as to oppose the change of flux.

Q7 A coil of 20 turns through which a flux of 1 Wb passed has this flux reduced to zero in 0.1 s. What emf would be induced across this coil? ◆

Q8 The coil in Question 7 has a cross-sectional area of 0.01 m^2 and is placed in a uniform magnetic field of magnetic flux density 1 T. Initially the coil's plane is perpendicular to the flux, but it is then rotated at 90° to it in 0.1 s. What emf is induced across this coil? ◆

In Exploration 2.1 you can use a solar motor to provide a measure of rate of flow. This motor is effectively a coil rotating in a magnetic field (see Figure 2.23). So, as it rotates, the magnetic flux linked with it changes.

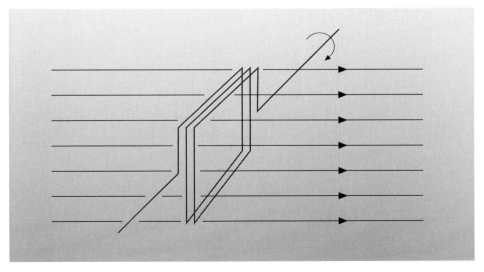

Figure 2.23
Rotating coil

E ▶ Exploration 2.1 Measuring liquid flow using a propeller meter

Apparatus:

◆ propeller mounted on a solar motor ◆ baseboard
◆ water pump ◆ cold feed and expansion tank ◆ measuring jug
◆ stopwatch ◆ voltmeter, oscilloscope, frequency meter, VELA, or computer and interface with software (as appropriate)

Ensure that mains operated equipment is well out of the way of splashes and spills

Outline

This sort of propeller meter would normally be found in a pipeline, not measuring free flow as in this investigation. It would be angled to the flow and have its bearings away from the liquid where they are less likely to be damaged or suffer from corrosion. It is easy to remove such a meter to inspect or replace it, even while liquid is flowing.

The spinning of the propeller drives the solar motor, here acting as a dynamo/generator. The dynamo/generator produces an electromotive force, emf, by virtue of the change of magnetic flux in its armature as it rotates. With a d.c. dynamo having just one rotating coil, the output emf is of the form shown in Figure 2.24

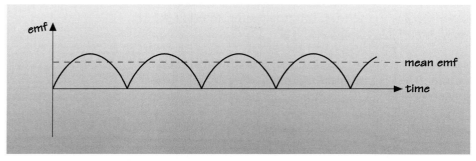

Figure 2.24 A d.c. dynamo trace

You can measure either (i) the frequency of this emf or (ii) mean emf. Frequency can be measured using an oscilloscope, a frequency meter, a VELA or a computer and interface running suitable software. Mean emf can be measured simply by connecting the output to a voltmeter.

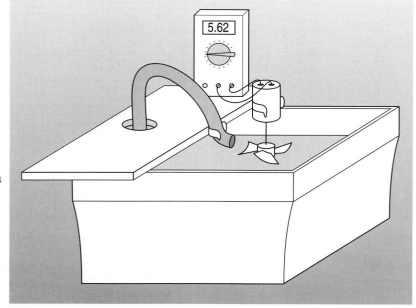

Figure 2.25
Propeller meter set-up

Instructions

The set-up for the propeller meter is shown in Figure 2.25.

Fill the tank with about 12 litres of water. Some tanks have a ridge in them, which is at about the 12 litre level. If yours is like this, fill to the ridge.

Switch on the pump and adjust the flow to the slowest rate possible. The adjuster is attached to the pump itself, so you will get your hands wet.

Adjust the angle of motor and propeller so that the water makes it spin at this low speed.

(i) To measure the frequency of the output emf, connect the motor to an appropriate frequency-measuring device and adjust until a steady trace or reading is given. Switch off the pump.

Draw up a table of results like Table 2.1(i) below.

(ii) To measure the mean emf, connect the motor to a voltmeter and adjust the range, if possible, until a fairly steady reading is seen. With a digital meter, where the last decimal place tends to flicker, you may have to take the reading that appears most often. Switch off the pump.

Draw up a table of results like Table 2.1(ii) below.

Switch the pump on again. Note the frequency or the mean emf being generated.

Table 2.1 Tables of results for Exploration 2.1

average frequency/Hz	time to collect 1 litre of water/s				average flow rate/litre s^{-1}
	first	second	third	average	

(i)

mean emf/V	time to collect 1 litre of water/s				average flow rate/litre s^{-1}
	first	second	third	average	

(ii)

Move the propeller out of the flow. Now record the time taken to collect 1 litre of water from the uninterrupted outflow. Do this three times, adding your results to the table on each occasion. Calculate the average time taken to collect 1 litre of water.

Alter the flow adjuster on the pump and obtain at least two more sets of collection times for 1 litre of water and the associated frequencies or emfs generated. Switch off the pump and disconnect the electrical circuit.

Calculate the average flow rate (litre s^{-1}). This is done by calculating the reciprocal of the collection time. Hence, if 1 litre of water was collected in an average of 5.9 seconds, the average flow rate would be $\dfrac{1}{5.9} = 0.17$ litre s^{-1}.

Plot a graph of either mean emf generated or average frequency against the average flow rate and report on how these are related.

Q9 The results in Table 2.2 were obtained of mean emf generated against average flow rate for a propeller meter. To what extent is direct proportionality shown between the mean emf generated and the average flow rate? ◆

A further investigation could also be made of how the angle of the propeller to the flow affects the mean emf generated or the frequency of the output voltage.

Table 2.2

Mean emf generated/V	Average flow rate/litre s^{-1}
0.13	0.15
0.17	0.17
0.19	0.21
0.21	0.22

Q10 The solar motor/generator of the propeller meter gave the oscilloscope trace shown in Figure 2.26.

The timebase was set at 10 ms div^{-1} and the gain/amplifier at 0.05 V div^{-1}.

(a) What was the frequency of the output from this solar motor/generator?

(b) What was the peak to peak output voltage being generated? ◆

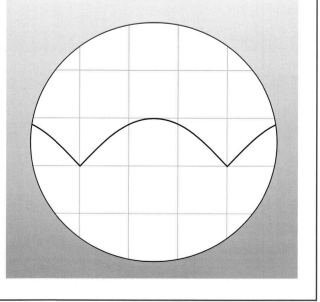

Figure 2.26 Oscilloscope trace

Some theory

To see how the change of magnetic flux associated with rotation affects the emf induced we will assume that the magnetic flux density is uniform within this device and so, if the coil has rotated so that the perpendicular to it has moved from being parallel to the flux to an angle of θ, then the flux linked with each turn is given by:

$$\phi = BA\cos\theta$$

If this coil is rotating at a constant angular velocity of ω (rad s^{-1}) then, after a time t (s), it will have rotated through an angle ωt, so

$$\phi = BA\cos\omega t \qquad (2.3)$$

From Neumann's equation we have:

$$E = -N\frac{\mathrm{d}\phi}{\mathrm{d}t}$$

combining this with Equation (2.3) gives

$$E = -N\frac{\mathrm{d}(BA\cos\omega t)}{\mathrm{d}t}$$

At this point calculus needs to be used to reach the final relationship:

$$E = NBA\omega\sin\omega t$$

(*Note:* Do not worry if you have not studied calculus.)

Hence the emf varies sinusoidally with time. If it was an a.c. dynamo with just one coil, then its output emf would be of the form shown in Figure 27.

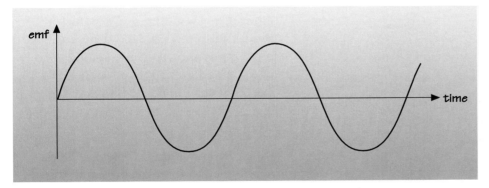

Figure 2.27
An a.c. dynamo trace

For a d.c. dynamo, the trace would look like the one shown in Figure 2.28.

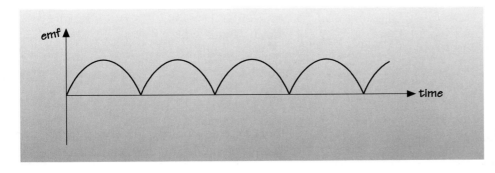

Figure 2.28
An d.c. dynamo trace

A voltmeter attached to the d.c. version would register a mean emf as illustrated by the dotted line.

2.8 The Hall effect

In 1879, Edwin Hall (1855–1938) devised an experiment to identify the sign of charge carriers in conductors. Today, devices based on what is known as the Hall effect are used extensively to measure the strength of magnetic fields and to make switches that have no mechanical parts.

When a charge q is placed in an electric field of **electric field strength** E, it experiences a force F, where

$$F = Bqv$$

Figure 2.29 shows a piece of semiconductor, drawn three times to illustrate this phenomenon. In Figure 2.29(a) the current is shown in the wires, but in the semiconductor material itself the charge carriers (electrons) are drawn so that we can show the effects of the magnetic field.

Figure 2.29
The Hall effect

Each of these moving charges constitutes a current and experiences a force from the vertical magnetic field drawn in Figure 2.29(b). The electrons are shown to be forced to the far side of the semiconductor.

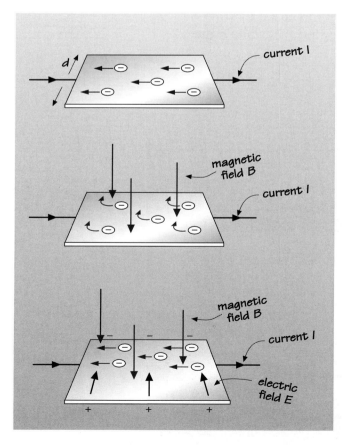

Figure 2.29(c) shows the electron current flowing along the far side, leaving the near side positively charged. This charge difference across the semiconductor produces an electric field from positive to negative as shown. The resulting potential difference is called the Hall potential difference, or Hall voltage, and can be measured directly with a voltmeter.

Each charge within this electric field experiences a force according to the relationship $F = Bqv$. The emf builds up across the semiconductor until the force on each electron from the magnetic field is balanced by the force from the electric field. That is when

$$Eq = Bqv$$

or

$$E = Bv$$

This expression links the electric and magnetic fields and can be used to find the magnetic flux density from the measured Hall voltage. To do this we need to write E a different way. You may already know that

$$E = \frac{V}{d}$$

so, we can write

$$\frac{V}{d} = Bv$$

and

$$V = Bvd$$

From this you can see that for a piece of semiconductor carrying a constant current, the Hall voltage is proportional to the magnetic flux density.

If you take your study of physics further, you are likely to cover more on semiconductors. You will then learn that we consider there to be positive charge carriers, called holes, as well as negative electrons, and that the Hall effect applies to these too.

The integrated circuit (i.c.) used in Exploration 2.2 senses the Hall voltage developed and provides an on/off or high/low output voltage according to its situation. In most cases the size and type of semiconductor material used in the integrated circuit will give a Hall voltage of microvolts or millivolts. The larger output voltages seen with these i.c.s is due to further amplification.

The same basic principles can be applied to the electromagnetic flow meter shown in Figure 2.30.

This consists of a pipe with an electromagnet positioned around it so as to generate a magnetic field across the pipe. Two electrodes are then

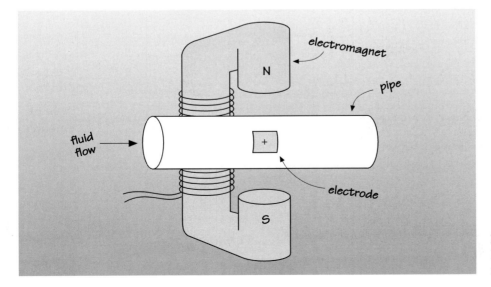

Figure 2.30
Electromagnetic flow meter

placed on opposite sides of the pipe and at 90° to the magnetic field. These electrodes are the equivalent of the front and back edges of the piece of semiconductor shown in Figure 2.29 in the development of the expression for the Hall voltage.

In this situation, the charge carriers are ions in the fluid that is flowing down the pipe. If we assume that these ions flow at the same speed, v, as the fluid, then a voltage will be produced across the electrodes given by:

$$V = Bvd$$

and we would say that this voltage has been induced by the movement of the ions in the magnetic field. An alternative way of looking at this is to think of a conducting strip of ions moving in the magnetic field and so inducing an emf across it. The resulting expression is just the same.

Q11 In his book *Experimental Researches in Electricity*, Michael Faraday describes how he tried to measure the voltage between two probes placed on opposite sides of the River Thames near Waterloo Bridge as the tide came in and out. He failed to detect any voltage at all. Suggest some reasons for this. ◆

Q12 The Thames near Waterloo Bridge is about 200 m wide. The vertical component of the Earth's magnetic field is approximately 4×10^{-5} T. If the maximum tidal flow was 5 m s^{-1}, (a) what is the maximum voltage you would expect to record across two probes placed one each side of the river and (b) why would this be a maximum? ◆

Q13 A magnetic field of flux density 1 T is provided across a pipe through which an ionic fluid flows. Two probes are positioned at 90° to this field at a separation of 0.1 m. If the fluid flows at a speed of 10 m s^{-1}, what voltage would you expect to record across the probes? ◆

The Thames at Waterloo Bridge

Exploration 2.2   Measuring liquid flow by a turbine meter with (i) a magnetic pickup or (ii) a Hall effect i.c. switch

Apparatus:

- magnet and turbine assembly on baseboard ◆ magnetic pick-up
- Hall effect i.c. switch ◆ water pump ◆ 4.5 V battery pack
- cold feed and expansion tank ◆ measuring jug ◆ stopwatch
- frequency meter, oscilloscope, VELA, or computer and interface with software (as appropriate)

50
MINUTES

Ensure that mains operated equipment is well out of the way of splashes and spills

As with the propeller meter, these transducers would normally be found in a pipeline, not measuring free flow as in these investigations. It would also be more common for the turbine to rotate perpendicular to the direction of flow of the liquid. However, the set-up here is easy to assemble and demonstrates the principle well.

The system consists of a freely rotating paddle-wheel containing a series of magnets. The movement of these magnets past (i) a magnetic pick-up and (ii) a Hall effect i.c. switch generates electrical pulses (see Figure 2.31).

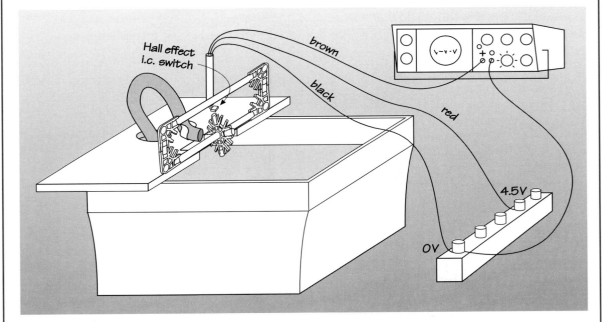

Figure 2.31   Apparatus and set-up of Hall effect i.c. switch

(i) Magnetic pick-up

As the magnets move past the transducer, changes in magnetic flux occur within its coil, resulting in a series of induced emfs being generated. These emfs can then be recorded in terms of their frequency.

(ii) Hall effect i.c. switch

The Hall effect comes about when a magnetic field is applied to the charge carriers within a conductor or semiconductor. The field causes the charge carriers to be displaced, so building up an electric field, which in turn gives rise to a voltage, the Hall voltage, across the specimen.

The integrated circuit used here senses the Hall voltage developed and provides an on/off or high/low output voltage according to its situation.

Fill the tank with about 12 litres of water. Some tanks have a ridge in them, which is at about the 12 litre level. If yours is like this, fill to the ridge.

Arrange (i) the magnetic pick-up or (ii) the Hall effect i.c. switch so that its end is within a few millimetres of the paddle-wheel's magnets as they rotate.

If the magnetic pick-up is being used, this can be connected directly to a frequency meter, an oscilloscope, a VELA or a computer and interface running the appropriate software. The Hall effect i.c. switch will need a battery connection. Note the connections required.

Position the paddle-wheel so that it is central on its axle. Switch the pump on and adjust its flow to the slowest rate possible. The adjuster is attached to the pump itself, so you will get your hands wet.

Adjust the position of the outflow pipe until the paddle-wheel spins easily. Switch off the pump.

Draw up a table of results like Table 2.3 below.

mean output frequency/Hz	time to collect 1 litre of water/s				average flow rate/litre s^{-1}
	first	second	third	average	

Table 2.3 Table of results for Exploration 2.2

Switch the pump on again. Note the mean output frequency of the pulses being generated.

Move the paddle-wheel to one side and record the time taken to collect 1 litre of water from the uninterrupted outflow. Do this three times, adding your results to the table on each occasion. Calculate the average time taken to collect 1 litre of water.

Alter the flow adjuster on the pump and obtain at least two more sets of collection times for 1 litre of the water and the associated mean output frequencies. Switch off the pump and disconnect the electrical circuits.

Calculate the average flow rate (litre s^{-1}). This is done by calculating the reciprocal of the collection time. Hence, if 1 litre of water was collected in an average of 5.9 seconds, the average flow rate would be $\dfrac{1}{5.9} = 0.17 \, \text{litre s}^{-1}$.

Plot a graph of the mean output frequency against the average flow rate.

Q14 Is there a linear relationship between the mean output frequency and the average flow rate? ◆

Q15 The blades of a commercial turbine meter are fixed inside a pipe and all the fluid flowing through the pipe has to pass over them. The turbine in our model acts more like the watermill wheels of previous centuries. What do you think is the main disadvantage of the model system that we have used? ◆

Q16 The set of results in Table 2.4 were obtained for a magnetic pick-up. Plot a graph of mean output frequency against the average flow rate and comment on the relationship between the two. ◆

A waterwheel

Table 2.4

Mean output frequency/Hz	Average flow rate/litre s^{-1}
12.510	0.147
13.620	0.162
15.810	0.192
18.870	0.226

Q17 The data in Table 2.5 overleaf relate to a Hall effect i.c. To what extent does this device appear to show a linear relationship between the magnetic flux density and the output voltage? ◆

Table 2.5

Magnetic flux density/$\times 10^{-4}$ T	Output voltage/V
1000.000	2.84
800.000	2.66
600.000	2.47
400.000	2.28
200.000	2.10
0.000	1.92

One of the easiest commercial flow sensors to understand is that marketed by RS Components as a flow transducer. It consists simply of a turbine that rotates with the passage of the liquid. As the blades of the turbine rotate, they block and unblock the passage of an infrared beam to a photodiode connected to an amplifier, a Schmitt trigger and an output transistor. This results in a pulsed output that can be measured on an oscilloscope, a frequency meter, a VELA or a computer with interface set up to measure frequency or display a waveform. The system is acting as a light gate, as in the measurement of time, speed and acceleration in dynamics investigations.

E ◆ **Exploration 2.3   Measuring liquid flow by an optical technique**

Apparatus:

- ◆ flow transducer ◆ 4.5 V battery pack ◆ water pump
- ◆ cold feed and expansion tank ◆ measuring jug ◆ stopwatch
- ◆ frequency meter, oscilloscope, VELA, or computer and interface with software (as appropriate) ◆ retort stand, clamp and boss

50 MINUTES

Ensure that mains operated equipment is well out of the way of splashes and spills

The equipment should be set up as shown in Figure 2.32.

So how exactly does this optical technique work? It is simply a case of the faster the rate of flow of the liquid, the faster the turbine spins inside the flow transducer, and the more often the turbine blade interrupts the infrared beam. This gives a higher frequency pulsed output.

The effect of the **Schmitt trigger** is to 'sharpen' the output, making a relatively slow change into one with a fast rise or fall time: it squares off the waveform. This enables the beginning and end of each waveform to be easily detected, which makes counting the number of waves each second possible. It also removes unwanted spikes from the signal.

Fill the tank with about 12 litres of water. Some tanks have a ridge in them, which is at about the 12 litre level. If yours is like this, fill to the ridge.

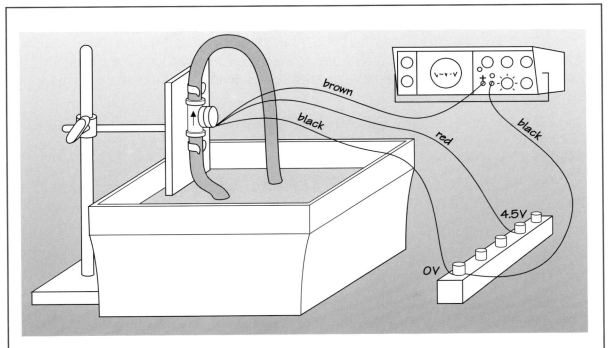

Figure 2.32 Experimental set-up for Exploration 2.3

Arrange the flow transducer so that it is vertically oriented with the arrow (for direction of flow) pointing vertically upwards. Ensure that the open end of the pipe points directly into the tank.

Connect the transducer to its battery supply and to a frequency meter, an oscilloscope, a VELA or a computer and interface running the appropriate software.

Switch on the pump and adjust the flow to the fastest rate possible. The adjuster is attached to the pump itself, so you will get your hands wet. Now switch off the pump.

Draw up a table of results like the Table 2.6 below

mean output frequency/Hz	time to collect 1 litre of water/s				average flow rate/litre s^{-1}
	first	second	third	average	

Table 2.6 Table of results for Exploration 2.3

Switch the pump on again. Note the frequency of the output pulses.

Now record the time taken to collect 1 litre of water from the outflow. Do this three times, adding your results to the table on each occasion. Calculate the average time taken to collect 1 litre of water.

Alter the flow adjuster on the pump and obtain at least two more sets of collection times for 1 litre of water and the associated mean output frequencies. Switch off the pump and disconnect the electrical circuits.

Calculate the average flow rate (litre s^{-1}). This is done by calculating the reciprocal of the collection time. Hence, if 1 litre of water was collected in an average of 5.9 seconds,

the average flow rate would be $\dfrac{1}{5.9} = 0.17\,litre\ s^{-1}$.

Plot a graph of the mean output frequency against the average flow rate.

Q18 Is there a linear relationship between the mean output frequency and the average flow rate? ◆

Repeat your investigation but with the flow transducer (i) horizontal and (ii) with its arrow pointing vertically downwards.

How does the orientation of the flow transducer affect the readings obtained?

Q19 Why might you think the orientation of the flow transducer could affect the readings obtained? ◆

The graph provided with the flow transducer is shown in Figure 2.33. How well does this match with your findings?

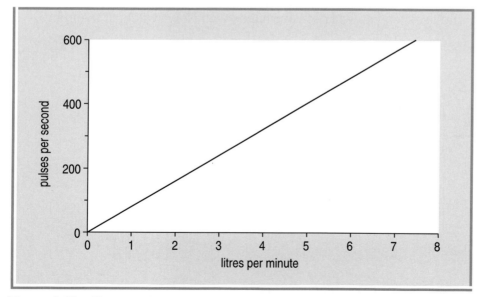

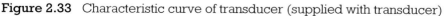

Figure 2.33   Characteristic curve of transducer (supplied with transducer)

Q20   The oscilloscope trace shown in Figure 2.34 was obtained using an optical flow sensor. The time-base was set at 1 ms div^{-1} and the gain/amplifier at 1 V div^{-1}.

(a) What was the frequency of the output from this sensor?

(b) If the line immediately below the trace represents 0 V, (i) what is the highest voltage shown and (ii) what is the lowest voltage shown? ◆

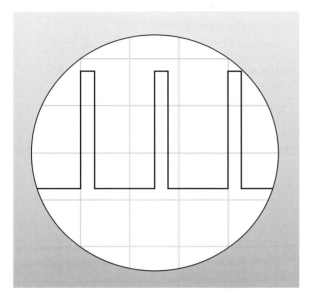

Figure 2.34
Oscilloscope trace
obtained using an optical
flow sensor

Achievements

After working through this section you should be able to:

- calculate the flow rate required for a fluid to transfer thermal energy at a known rate
- describe the difference between open-loop and closed-loop systems for controlling fluid flow
- explain that a pressure difference (or pressure gradient) is needed to make a fluid flow
- show that the work done transferring a unit volume of a liquid is equal to the pressure drop needed for that transfer
- describe the difference between a centrifugal pump, a peristaltic pump and a compressor
- explain how valves can be used to control the pressure of a fluid
- describe how to alter the power output of an electrical pump.

Glossary

Bimetallic strip A strip made from two different metals fastened together. The metals expand at different rates, so the shape of the strip varies with its temperature.

Centrifugal pump A pump that operates by spinning a fluid around in a chamber. Fluid enters the centre of the chamber (along the axis of rotation) at a low pressure and leaves from the edge at a high pressure.

Compressor A pump employing a piston moving in a cylinder. Commonly used for pumping gases and in refrigeration units.

Electric field strength The force acting per coulomb of charge (i.e. per unit charge) on a charge placed in the electric field. It is measured in units of $V\ m^{-1}$

(from $E = \dfrac{V}{d}$) or $N\ C^{-1}$ (from $E = \dfrac{F}{q}$)

Electromagnetic induction The phenomenon of electricity being generated when an electrical conductor is moved in a magnetic field. It is used in the design of dynamos and alternators.

Fluid speed The average speed of a fluid in a pipe or channel, defined as the volume flow rate divided by the cross-sectional area.

Hall effect The creation of an electric field when a magnetic field is applied to the charge carriers within a conductor or semiconductor. The direction of this field is given by Flemming's left-hand rule.

Induced emf When an electrical conductor is moved in the field of a magnet, electricity is generated (see *electromagnetic induction*). The voltage generated in this way is called the induced emf or electromotive force. Although it is a voltage, the historical terminology, which implies it is a force pushing the electricity, has been retained. It is much more common to refer to 'emf' than to 'electromotive force'.

Magnetic flux density, *B* Unit: tesla (T). This is a measure of the strength of a magnetic field. Magnetic fields are represented diagrammatically by lines; you can think of the magnetic flux density as the number of lines passing through unit area perpendicular to the lines themselves. It does not take any account of the physical size of the magnet. Also called magnetic induction.

Mass flow rate The mass of fluid entering or leaving a pipe or channel in one second.

Negative feedback   A process in which an increase in the output of a system causes a decrease in the input, and vice versa.

Peristaltic pump   A pump that raises the pressure of a fluid by squeezing it down a flexible tube.

Rotary pump   A pump that uses energy from a rotating shaft to increase the pressure of a fluid.

Solenoid valve   A valve consisting of an iron slug in a solenoid coil. When electricity flows in the coil the valve opens, when there is no electricity the valve closes.

Schmitt trigger   A circuit used to sharpen the output from a system before it is fed into a computer or oscilloscope. It squares off the waveform, which makes the beginning and end of each waveform easier to detect. It also removes unwanted spikes from the signal.

Thermocouple   A temperature sensor made from the junction of two different metals.

Thermostat   A switch that maintains a constant temperature by turning a system on when the temperature falls below a certain value and turning it off when when the temperature rises above this value.

Throttle valve   A valve that can be used for fine control of the pressure of fluids in a pipe

Triac   An electronic component that can be used to control the power delivered to pumps run off alternating current supplies.

Valve   A tap used to control the flow of fluid through a pipe.

Volume flow rate   The volume of fluid entering or leaving a system per second.

Answers to Ready to Study test

R1

$$P = 100\,\text{kPa}$$
$$= 100 \times 10^3\,\text{Pa}$$

and

$$A = 21\,\text{cm} \times 30\,\text{cm}$$
$$= 21 \times 10^{-2}\,\text{m} \times 30 \times 10^{-2}\,\text{m}$$
$$= 6.3 \times 10^{-2}\,\text{m}^2$$

$$P = \frac{F}{A}$$

so

$$F = PA$$
$$= 100 \times 10^3\,\text{Pa} \times 6.3 \times 10^{-2}\,\text{m}^2$$
$$= 6.3 \times 10^3\,\text{N}$$

R2

Liquids have a fixed volume but no fixed shape and will flow to the lowest point of a container. This behaviour occurs because the molecules in a liquid have to remain, on average, a certain distance from their neighbours, but are otherwise free to move around.

A gas does not having a fixed volume, it is less dense the higher it is and it has no fixed shape – its fast-moving molecules move freely until they collide with another molecule or a boundary. A gas has these properties because the molecules of gases are considered to be completely independent of each other.

Table 2.7 summarises the properties of fluids.

Table 2.7 The properties of fluids

	Liquid	Gas
Volume	Fixed	Not fixed
Shape	Not fixed	Not fixed
Movement	Flows to lowest part	Fills space available
Molecules	Not completely free	Completely independent of each other
Effect of heating	Expands	Expands

R3

We use $E = Fs$ to find the work done when a force F (N) moves through a distance s (m). We are told that the speed $v = 10 \text{ m s}^{-1}$ and know that

$$\text{speed} = \frac{\text{distance travelled}}{\text{time taken}}$$

or

$$v = \frac{s}{t}$$

Rearranging gives $s = vt$ so
$E = Fvt$

$$= 500 \text{ N} \times 10 \text{ms}^{-1} \times 60 \text{ s}$$

$$= 300000 \text{ N m}$$

$$= 3.0 \times 10^5 \text{ J}$$

R4

$$P = IV = 5 \text{ A} \times 240 \text{ V} = 1200 \text{ W}$$

R5

$P = VI$
$R_{\text{total}} = 10 \Omega + 20 \Omega = 30 \Omega$

$$R = \frac{V}{I}$$

so, the current flowing through the 10 Ω resistor is

$$I_{10\Omega} = \frac{V}{R}$$

$$= \frac{12 \text{ V}}{30 \Omega}$$

$$= 0.40 \text{ A}$$

and the potential difference across it is

$$V_{10\Omega} = IR$$

$$= 0.40 \text{ A} \times 10 \Omega$$

$$= 4.0 \text{ V}$$

So, thermal energy is transferred to it at the rate

$$P_{10\Omega} = VI$$

$$= 4.0 \text{ V} \times 0.40 \text{ A}$$

$$= 1.6 \text{ W}$$

R6

We can calculate change of energy using the equation

$$\Delta E = mc\Delta T$$

We know that

$$\Delta T = 60°C - 20°C$$

$$= 40°C$$

$$= 40 \text{ K}$$

and

$$C = 4.2 \text{ kJ kg}^{-1} \text{ K}^{-1}$$

$$= 4.2 \times 10^3 \text{ J kg}^{-1} \text{ K}^{-1}$$

Therefore

$$\Delta E = 5 \text{ kg} \times 4.2 \times 10^3 \text{ J kg}^{-1} \text{ K}^{-1} \times 40 \text{ K}$$

$$= 8.4 \times 10^5 \text{ J}$$

R7

$$\rho = \frac{m}{v} = \frac{1500\,\text{kg}}{1\,\text{m}^3} = 1500\,\text{kg}\,\text{m}^{-3}$$

R8

$$P = \frac{E}{t}$$

$$E = Pt = 1200\,\text{W} \times 3 \times 60\,\text{s} = 216000\,\text{J}$$

Answers to questions in the text

Q1

$$P = 2.0\,\text{kW}$$

$$= 2.0 \times 10^3\,\text{J}\,\text{s}^{-1}$$

$$\Delta E = mc\Delta T$$

and

$$P = \frac{\Delta E}{\Delta t}$$

so

$$P = \frac{mc\Delta T}{\Delta t}$$

and rearranging gives

$$\frac{m}{\Delta t} = \frac{P}{c\Delta T}$$

We know that

$$c = 4.2 \times 10^3\,\text{J}\,\text{kg}^{-1}\,\text{K}^{-1}$$

and

$$\Delta T = 60^\circ\text{C} - 40^\circ\text{C}$$

$$= 20\,\text{K}$$

therefore

$$\frac{m}{\Delta t} = \frac{2.0 \times 10^3\,\text{J}\,\text{s}^{-1}}{4.2 \times 10^3\,\text{J}\,\text{kg}^{-1} \times 20\,\text{K}}$$

$$= 2.4 \times 10^{-2}\,\text{kg}\,\text{s}^{-1}$$

(to two significant figures)

Q2

Volume flow rate = speed
× cross-sectional area

so

$$\frac{\Delta V}{\Delta t} = 0.60\,\text{m}^2 \times 5.0\,\text{m}\,\text{s}^{-1}$$

$$= 3.0\,\text{m}^3\,\text{s}^{-1}$$

Density is given by

$$\rho = \frac{m}{V}$$

so

$$m = \rho V$$

Therefore mass flow rate is given by

$$\frac{m}{\Delta t} = \rho\frac{V}{\Delta t}$$

$$= 1.2\,\text{kg}\,\text{m}^{-3} \times 3.0\,\text{m}^3\,\text{s}^{-1}$$

$$= 3.6\,\text{kg}\,\text{s}^{-1}$$

Q3

Volume flow rate = speed
× cross-sectional area

$$A = \pi r^2$$

$$= \pi\left(6.5 \times 10^{-3}\,\text{m}\right)^2$$

$$= 1.33 \times 10^{-4}\,\text{m}^2$$

$$\rho = \frac{m}{V}$$

so

$$V = \frac{m}{\rho}$$

$$= \frac{2.5 \times 10^{-3}\,\text{kg}}{1.0 \times 10^3\,\text{kg}\,\text{m}^{-3}}$$

$$= 2.5 \times 10^{-6}\,\text{m}^3$$

Therefore

$$\frac{\Delta V}{\Delta t} = 2.5 \times 10^{-6} \, \text{m}^3 \, \text{s}^{-1}$$

so

$$vA = 2.5 \times 10^{-6} \, \text{m}^3 \, \text{s}^{-1}$$

and

$$v = \frac{2.5 \times 10^{-6} \, \text{m}^3 \, \text{s}^{-1}}{A}$$

$$= \frac{2.5 \times 10^{-6} \, \text{m}^3 \, \text{s}^{-1}}{1.33 \times 10^{-4} \, \text{m}^2}$$

$$= 1.88 \times 10^{-2} \, \text{m s}^{-1}$$

$$= 0.02 \, \text{m s}^{-1} \text{ (to two significant figures)}$$

Q4

$$P = \frac{F}{A}$$

$$A = \pi r^2$$

$$= \pi \left(1.25 \times 10^{-2} \, \text{m}\right)^2$$

$$= 4.9 \times 10^{-4} \, \text{m}^2$$

so

$$P = \frac{5.0 \, \text{N}}{4.9 \times 10^{-4} \, \text{m}^2}$$

$$= 1.02 \times 10^4 \, \text{Pa}$$

$$= 10 \, \text{kPa} \text{ (to two significant figures)}$$

The liquid inside the syringe was already at the same pressure as the air outside – atmospheric pressure. So, the pressure calculated is the additional pressure at the syringe end of the needle that will cause the liquid to flow out.

Q5

$$\Delta E = V \Delta P$$

$$\Delta P = 10 \, \text{kPa}$$

$$= 10 \times 10^3 \, \text{Pa}$$

and

$$V = 25 \, \text{cm}^3$$

$$= 25 \times 10^{-6} \, \text{m}^3$$

so

$$\Delta E = 25 \times 10^{-6} \, \text{m}^3 \times 10 \times 10^3 \, \text{Pa}$$

$$= 0.25 \, \text{J}$$

Q6

$$P = \rho g h$$

$$= 1.0 \times 10^3 \, \text{kg m}^{-3} \times 9.8 \, \text{N kg}^{-1} \times 5.0 \, \text{m}$$

$$= 4.9 \times 10^4 \, \text{Pa}$$

Q7

The change of flux is −1 Wb. So, with

$$E = -N \frac{d\phi}{dt}$$

we have

$$E = -20 \times \frac{-1 \, \text{Wb}}{0.1 \, \text{s}}$$

$$= 200 \, \text{V}$$

Q8

The initial magnetic flux will be

$$BA = 1 \, \text{T} \times 0.01 \, \text{m}^2$$

$$= 0.01 \, \text{Wb}$$

The final flux will be zero. Hence the magnetic flux will have changed by −0.01 Wb. So

$$E = -N\frac{d\theta}{dt}$$

$$= -20 \times \frac{-0.01\,\text{Wb}}{0.1\,\text{s}}$$

$$= 2\,\text{V}$$

Q9

See Figure 2.35. For the four points plotted, the best-fit line does appear to be straight and pass through the origin. Hence, direct proportionality is shown within the limits of the uncertainty of these results. At very slow flow rates the propeller just did not turn and so no readings could be taken.

Q10

(a) There are three divisions along the x-axis between identical parts of the trace and so a time of 3×10 ms, or 30×10^{-3} s, is between them.

The frequency is the number of complete waveforms produced each second and so is given by

$$\text{frequency} = \frac{1}{\text{time to display each waveform}}$$

So

$$\text{frequency} = \frac{1}{30 \times 10^{-3}\,\text{s}}$$

$$= \frac{1 \times 10^3\,\text{s}^{-1}}{30}$$

$$= 33.3\,\text{Hz}$$

(b) The trace occupies just 1 division along the y-axis, so the peak-to-peak voltage is given by

$$1\,\text{div} \times 0.05\,\text{V div}^{-1} = 0.05\,\text{V}$$

Q11

There are a number of possibilities, any combination of which may have been true:

- the voltmeter that he had access to may not have been sensitive enough
- the magnetic field may have been too weak to produce a high enough voltage to detect
- the flow speed may have been too low to produce a high enough voltage to detect.

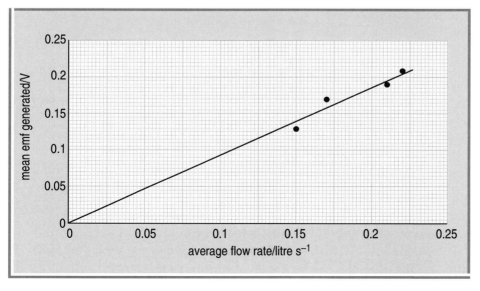

Figure 2.35
Answer to Question 9

Q12

(a) Since

$$V = Bvd$$

we have

$$V = 4 \times 10^{-5}\,\text{T} \times 5\,\text{ms}^{-1} \times 200\,\text{m}$$

$$= 4 \times 10^{-2}\,\text{V}$$

(b) This is a maximum value as tidal flow reduces to zero and then reverses.

Q13

Since

$$V = Bvd$$

we have

$$V = 1\,\text{T} \times 10\,\text{ms}^{-1} \times 0.1\,\text{m}$$

$$= 1\,\text{V}$$

Q14

This will depend on your graph, but it is likely that direct proportionality will be displayed between the mean output frequency and the average flow rate.

Q15

We cannot be sure that all the water flowing out of the pipe is actually moving the paddle-wheel round. Some 'escapes' to each side.

Q16

See Figure 2.36. The graph shows direct proportionality between the mean output frequency and the average flow rate – it is a straight line through the origin.

Q17

See Figure 2.37. The graph shows a linear relationship between the magnetic flux density and the output voltage for all values. However, they are not directly proportional to each other as, although the graph is a straight line, it does not pass through the origin.

Q18

This will depend on your results, but you probably found a linear relationship but not direct proportionality.

Q19

Bubbles often affect the readings. The pumps are designed to be used in the vertical plane where bubbles would escape through the system early on. Bubbles cause a change in the path of the infrared beam and so alter the number of pulses detected. Bends in pipes also affect the flow if they are near the transducer, tending to change the flow rate across the pipe.

Q20

(a) There are 1.5 divisions between identical parts of the trace along the x-axis and so a time of 1.5×1 ms, or 1.5×10^{-3} s, is between them.

The frequency is the number of complete waveforms produced each second and is given by

$$\text{frequency} = \frac{1}{\text{time to display each waveform}}$$

So

$$\text{frequency} = \frac{1}{1.5 \times 10^{-3}\,\text{s}}$$

$$= \frac{1 \times 10^{3}\,\text{s}^{-1}}{1.5}$$

$$= 667\,\text{Hz}$$

(b) (i) The upper level of the waveform is 2.75 divisions above the 0 V line. So, at 1 V div^{-1}, this must show $2.75 \times 1\,\text{V} = 2.75$ V.

(ii) The lower level of the trace is around 0.25 divisions above the 0 V line. So, at 1 V div^{-1}, this must show $0.25 \times 1\,\text{V} = 0.25$ V.

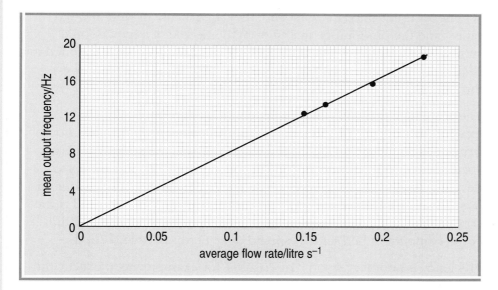

Figure 2.36 Answer to Question 16

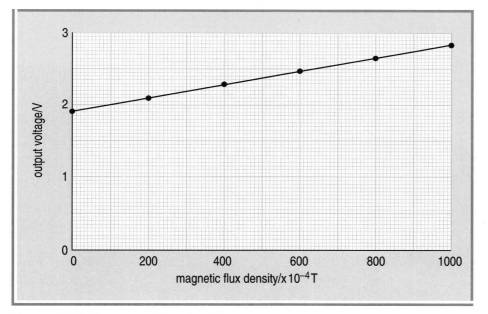

Figure 2.37 Answer to Question 17

3

MOVING FLUIDS THROUGH PIPES

Whenever fluids need to be moved, they are usually moved through pipes, and the pipes range in size from the needle of a hypodermic syringe to oil pipelines that are hundreds of miles long. As mentioned in Section 2, we generally need to be able to control how fluids move through pipes and to measure the rate of flow.

There are many reasons that we need to control flow. Safety, for example. If you have studied the SLIPP unit *Physics on the Move*, you may recall from Section 9.3 'Safety with fuels' that transferring fuels at speed produces charge separation that causes dangerous voltages to develop. So, flow rates need to be monitored to ensure safe transfer. In hospitals, it is vital that the correct dosages of drugs are delivered at the correct rates. Similarly, in agriculture, farmers need to ensure that the correct amount of herbicide is spread over a crop in each second.

Efficiency is another reason. Car engines, for example, need exactly the right amounts of petrol and air delivered to ensure efficient operation.

In other cases, the information may be required for billing the customer, or to check the calibration of a water pump for a central heating system or washing machine.

Pipes and
meters

So, this section is all about controlling and measuring rates of fluid flow through pipes. There are a large number of explorations and you will probably not have time to conduct them all. It would therefore be a good idea to divide them between the members of your group and then share your results and conclusions. Many of the explorations have detailed instructions – follow these carefully and, if you are still unsure of what to do, or why, ask your tutor for advice.

READY TO STUDY TEST

Before you begin this section you should be able to:

- describe and use the relationship $V = IR$
- state the relationship between resistance and length
- describe how resistance depends on temperature
- do specific heat capacity calculations
- interpret straight-line graphs
- describe and calculate kinetic energy and gravitational potential energy
- explain how pressure depends on force and area
- use the formula for kinetic energy

$$E_k = \frac{1}{2}mv^2$$

QUESTIONS

R1 (a) What current flows when a bulb that operates at 960 Ω, 240 V is operating?
(b) What resistance is needed in a circuit to draw 2 A from a 12 V supply?

R2 (a) Describe a graph of voltage plotted against current for a fixed resistance.
(b) If the same resistance has a constant voltage across it how does its resistance change with increasing temperature?

R3 One piece of resistance wire has a resistance of 12 Ω.

(a) What is the resistance of a piece of identical wire five times the length?
(b) If the original piece of wire is cut into four equal parts, what is the resistance of each?

R4 What is the kinetic energy of a 0.1 kg ball moving at 2 m s^{-1}?

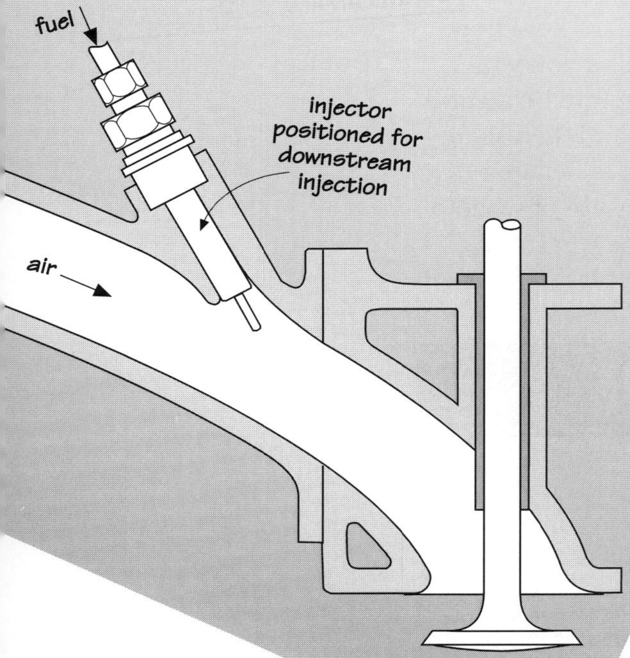

3.1 Air flow and engine efficiency

As you may already know, fuel-injection systems for motor vehicles have been in existence for more than forty years. The basic layout is shown in Figure 3.1. Their forerunner involved mixing air and petrol in a carburettor before passing the mixture into the cylinders to be ignited. Fuel-injection systems deliver a precise amount of atomized fuel (i.e. fuel in fine droplet form) to each inlet valve of the engine to be mixed with the incoming air. The results, when compared with carburettor systems, are:

- lower exhaust pollution
- lower fuel consumption
- higher power output
- smoother engine operation
- automatic adjustment of the air/fuel ratio to suit operating conditions.

Figure 3.1
Fuel injector

However, it can be difficult to get the right amount of fuel mixed with the incoming air and that is dependent on the amount of air entering each second: its flow rate. So how can flow rates be measured?

One way is to use the cooling effect of the moving fluid. You have probably blown across the top of a hot cup of tea or coffee to cool it. Blowing air past a heated metal filament has the same effect: it cools the filament. However, the act of cooling metallic conductors also changes their electrical resistance. This phenomenon is utilized in a **hot-wire anemometer**, which measures the speed of moving air by detecting the changing electrical resistance of a metallic conductor in the path of the air.

So how does the hot-wire anemometer work? The main part of it is based on a Wheatstone bridge, popularized by Professor Sir Charles Wheatstone in 1843, although not actually invented by him. Its circuit is shown in Figure 3.2.

One arrangement is to set up the circuit so that the voltmeter reads zero. In that case, the current I_1 through resistor R_1 and the current I_2 through resistor R_2 must be equal. If these currents are not equal, then a current would have to flow through the voltmeter and it would then display a non-zero value. Likewise, currents I_3 and I_4 would also have to be equal to each other, but not necessarily equal to I_1 and I_2. This situation is known as the balanced bridge.

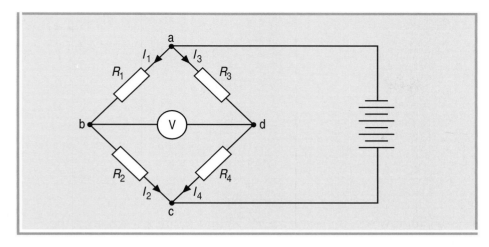

Figure 3.2
A Wheatstone
bridge circuit

With zero potential difference across bd, the voltages across ab and ad
must be equal to each other. Hence

$$V_{ab} = V_{ad}$$

and similarly

$$V_{bc} = V_{dc}$$

You will recall that $V = IR$, so we can now write

$$V_{ab} = I_1 R_1 = V_{ad} = I_3 R_3$$

therefore

$$I_1 R_1 = I_3 R_3$$

and

$$\frac{R_1}{R_3} = \frac{I_3}{I_1}$$

and also

$$V_{bc} = I_2 R_2 = V_{dc} = I_4 R_4$$

therefore

$$I_2 R_2 = I_4 R_4$$

and

$$\frac{R_2}{R_4} = \frac{I_4}{I_2}$$

However, $I_1 = I_2$ and $I_3 = I_4$ so, substituting for I_1 where $I_1 = I_2$, and for I_3
where $I_3 = I_4$, we have

$$\frac{R_1}{R_3} = \frac{I_4}{I_2}$$

and

$$\frac{R_2}{R_4} = \frac{I_4}{I_2}$$

so

$$\frac{R_1}{R_3} = \frac{R_2}{R_4}$$

and

$$R_1 = \frac{R_2 R_3}{R_4}$$

As you can now see, if resistances R_2, R_3 and R_4 are known, then the value of R_1 can be calculated.

Q1 Calculate the value of an unknown resistor R_1 if $R_2 = 10\ \Omega$, $R_3 = 5\ \Omega$ and $R_4 = 25\ \Omega$. Assume that the bridge circuit is balanced. ◆

At this stage you could use the Wheatstone bridge principle to see how a precision temperature sensing resistor could be used to measure temperature. In the arrangement shown in Figure 3.3 you would initially have the Wheatstone bridge in its balanced state. The hot-wire anemometer uses it in an unbalanced state. You will see the effect of the latter when you do, or hear a report on, Exploration 3.2, using the precision sensing resistor with an unbalanced bridge.

With the hot-wire anemometer, any increase in the speed of the incoming air will cause the metal filament to cool – more energy will be transferred from it to the air each second. As it cools, its resistance will decrease and so unbalance the bridge. This unbalanced bridge now feeds two voltages into a **differential amplifier**, a device whose output is the voltage

Figure 3.3
A hot-wire
anemometer circuit

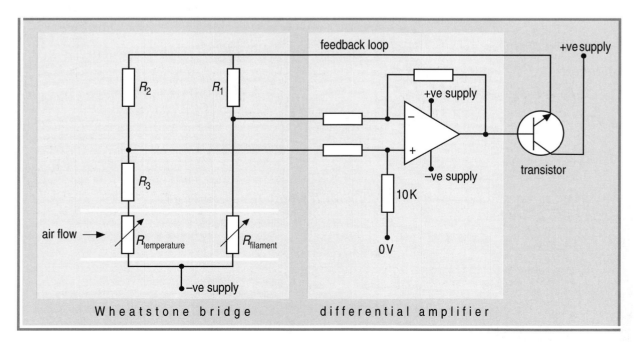

Wheatstone bridge   differential amplifier

difference between its inputs. This output voltage is then amplified by the transistor which, by means of the feedback loop, increases the voltage applied to the bridge (and the filament) until the filament returns to its original temperature and resistance. The voltage across the bridge therefore gives an indication of the air speed. The filament in a hot-wire anemometer is usually made of platinum, though more robust versions are now made using either platinum film resistors or thermistors.

Chladni's figures

In the fuel injection system of a motor vehicle, it is more common to measure the voltage across the resistor R_1, and various values of this voltage would be stored in a 'look-up table' in the electronic control unit or ECU (a computer) and from these the amount of fuel to be injected would be calculated to give the correct fuel to air ratio.

In practical applications, systems using a hot-wire anemometer also take account of changes of the input air temperature, as these would also unbalance the bridge. Resistor $R_{temperature}$ (as shown in Figure 3.3) compensates for changes in air temperature. Why do changes of the input air temperature need to be taken account of? In what circumstances would failing to do so cause problems?

If changes of the input air temperature were not taken account of then the system would adjust itself for different temperatures of the incoming air rather than for varying rates of flow. Problems would occur in environments which were appreciably hotter or colder than that in which the system had been set up.

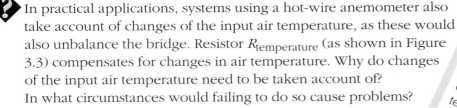

The original idea of using electricity and magnetism for telegraphy was put forward by the French physicist André Ampère in 1820, and the first apparatus devised by the Russian diplomat Baron Pavel Schilling in 1832. William Cooke, a demobilized officer from the Indian army, tried to perfect Schilling's device in 1836 but, faced with problems, joined forces with Wheatstone. They jointly patented their telegraph system in 1837.

PROFESSOR SIR CHARLES WHEATSTONE (1802–75)

Professor Sir Charles Wheatstone was a very productive inventor and much of his work was geared to perfecting long-distance telegraphy: sending telegrams over long distances by using electric signals. He is also credited with the design of a stereoscope to provide a 3-D effect, devising high-speed clocks with which to measure the speeds of cannon shot and an explanation for Chladni's figures – the patterns produced in sand when flat plates are vibrated. His work on these gained him admission to the Royal Society in 1832. He received many honours, including a knighthood and, in 1868, the Royal Society's highest award – the Copley Medal. An exhibition of some of his inventions can be seen at King's College in the Strand in London.

Wheatstone's Alphabet-Dial Telegraph (1858)

Charles Wheatstone

Some theoretical background

Kinetic theory, developed by Daniel Bernoulli (1700–82), links a rise in temperature to an increase in the amplitude of the vibration of the ions that make up a metal's crystal lattice. This increases the frequency of collision or interaction of these ions with the free electrons drifting along the wire. The increased rate of collision reduces the **average drift velocity** and so the current falls. Less current indicates a higher resistance. You can find a fuller explanation of kinetic theory on pages 183–8 of the SLIPP unit *Physics for Sport*.

In semiconductors, such as silicon, germanium and gallium arsenide, an increase in the amplitude of vibration of the atoms still occurs. However, as the temperature of these materials increases, they release more free electrons to drift along the material and so more than compensate for the reduction in drift velocity caused by the increase in frequency of collisions. Hence a larger current flows and the resistance of the material is lowered.

When a material shows no resistance at all it is called a superconductor and can only be fully described with quantum theory. (Quantum theory is discussed in Section 3 of the SLIPP unit *Physics in Space*, and you will probably learn more about it if you take your study of physics further.)

Now do Exploration 3.1 to gain experience of using a balanced Wheatstone bridge.

50
MINUTES

Safety goggles must be worn to protect your eyes.

E Exploration 3.1
Using a balanced Wheatstone bridge

Apparatus:

◆ 1 m of approximately $10\,\Omega\,\text{m}^{-1}$ wire mounted on a wooden lath ◆ 6 V d.c. power supply ◆ precision temperature sensing resistor PRC100 on long leads (RS 341-452) ◆ $100\,\Omega$ resistor (RS 158-086) ◆ tapping key ◆ metre rule ◆ sensitive galvanometer/voltmeter ◆ connecting leads ◆ 400 ml beaker ◆ −5 to 110°C thermometer ◆ Bunsen burner ◆ tripod ◆ gauze ◆ Asbestolux mat ◆ stirrer (if thermometer is not of stirring type) ◆ water ◆ ice

Calculating the resistance of a temperature sensing resistor by using a balanced Wheatstone bridge is quite a simple task. Here you will find how the resistance of the resistor changes for a range of temperatures between around 0°C and 100°C.

Set up the circuit shown in Figure 3.4 and switch on.

Half fill the beaker with water and add some ice, then place the temperature sensing resistor into the beaker. Allow the temperature to stabilize to about 0°C. Stir the water and ice mixture.

Draw a table for your results like Table 3.1.

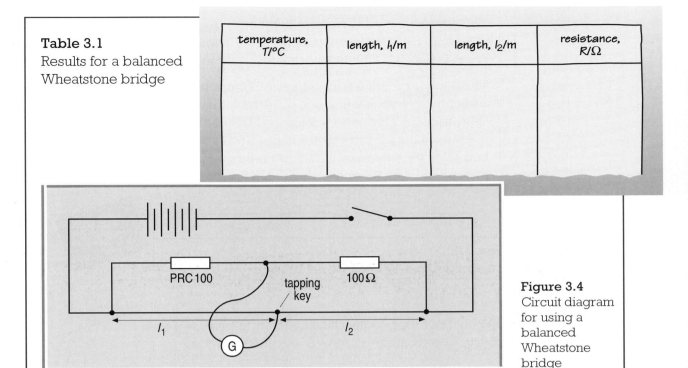

temperature, $T/°C$	length, l_1/m	length, l_2/m	resistance, R/Ω

Table 3.1
Results for a balanced
Wheatstone bridge

Figure 3.4
Circuit diagram
for using a
balanced
Wheatstone
bridge

Balance the bridge by moving the tapping key along the wire until the galvanometer shows no deflection. Measure the lengths of wire l_1 and l_2 and record them in your results table together with the temperature of the water.

Switch off the power supply, remove the temperature sensor and heat the water to around 10°C. Stir and allow the temperature to stabilize. Replace the temperature sensor and switch on the power supply again, balance the bridge and record the new lengths l_1 and l_2 together with the new temperature of the water.

Continue the process for a range of temperatures up to the boiling point of water.

Calculate the resistance of the temperature sensing resistor for each recorded temperature from

$$\frac{\text{resistance of PRC100}}{100\,\Omega} = \frac{l_1}{l_2}$$

or

$$\text{resistance of PRC100} = \frac{l_1}{l_2} \times 100\,\Omega$$

and add the value to the table. We can use the lengths l_1 and l_2 in this way as they are proportional to their resistance: the wire is the same diameter for the whole of its length.

Q2 How linear is the change of resistance of PRC100 with temperature? ◆

Q3 Why must one be careful just to touch the tapping key on to the wire rather than scraping it along? ◆

You now have a calibrated temperature sensor. With the data collected you could use this set-up to measure temperatures accurately within the range 0°C to 100°C. You have made a resistance thermometer.

The hot-wire anemometer set-up uses the Wheatstone bridge but in an *unbalanced* state. Exploration 3.2 gives a method for using the Wheatstone bridge as an unbalanced bridge. The arrangement is fundamentally the same as for the balanced bridge, except that instead of balancing the bridge by moving a tapping key along the wire you just measure the voltage across the bridge for a range of temperatures.

---

50 MINUTES

E **Exploration 3.2**
Using an unbalanced Wheatstone bridge

Safety goggles must be worn to protect your eyes.

Apparatus:

◆ as for Exploration 3.1, but replace the galvanometer (if you used one) and the tapping key with ◆ voltmeter, 0–10 V ◆ crocodile clip

Set up the circuit shown in Figure 3.5.

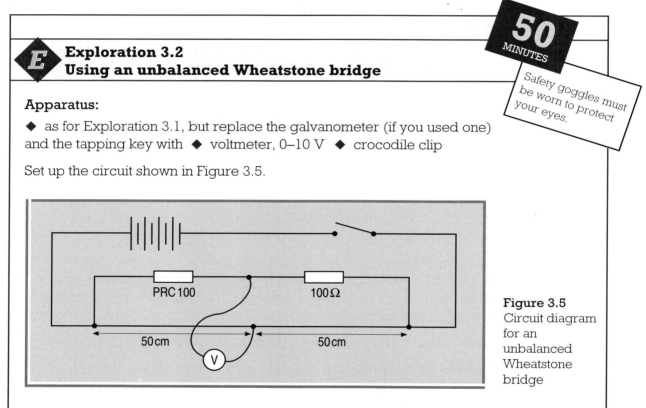

Figure 3.5
Circuit diagram for an unbalanced Wheatstone bridge

Switch on the supply and place the temperature sensing resistor into water to which ice has been added. Stir the mixture and allow the temperature to stabilize to about 0°C.

Record the temperature and the voltmeter reading.

Switch off the power supply, remove the temperature sensing resistor and now heat the water to around 10°C. Again, stir well and allow the temperature to stabilize. Replace the temperature sensing resistor and switch the power supply on again. Record the temperature and the voltmeter reading.

Continue the process to obtain voltmeter readings for a range of temperatures up to the boiling point of water.

Q4 How linearly does the voltage change with temperature? ◆

The next exploration enables you to calibrate a hot-wire anemometer, and Exploration 3.4 suggests some ways you can use it.

E Exploration 3.3 Calibrating a hot-wire anemometer

Apparatus:

◆ hot-wire anemometer (mounted on a board) and control box ◆ 6 V battery (RS 592-149) ◆ voltmeter, 0–5 V ◆ cylinder vacuum cleaner or air compressor ◆ variac or drill speed controller ◆ vernier callipers or vernier microscope ◆ connecting tubing and bungs ◆ stopwatch (for British Gas laboratory gas meter only) ◆ spirit-level (for Loflow meters only) ◆ leads ◆ heavy slotted base (Griffin and George STA-395-W) ◆ calibrated air flow meter (British Gas laboratory gas meter or Loflow meters Griffin and George FJC-700-100D and FJC-700-110A)

Place the board holding the anemometer pipe assembly into the heavy slotted base.

If you are using a British Gas laboratory gas meter, connect its outflow into the pipe's left-hand end, keeping the connecting tubing as straight and short as possible. If you are using a Loflow meter, connect its outflow end (top) into the pipe's left-hand end, bending the connecting tubing as little as possible (any bends will produce some turbulence and so reduce the overall rate of flow of the air). Figure 3.6 shows the experimental set-up.

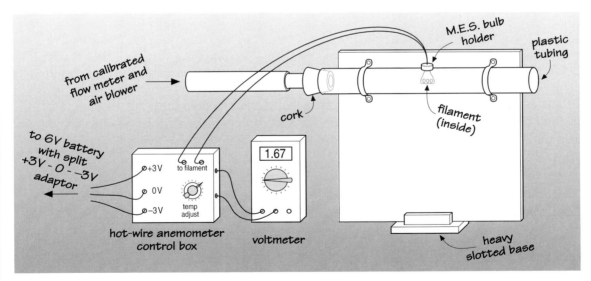

Figure 3.6 Experimental set-up for Exploration 3.3

Connect the outflow from the vacuum cleaner (blow end), or compressor, into the British Gas laboratory gas meter's input. Again, keep the piping as straight and short as possible. Or connect the outflow from the vacuum cleaner (blow end), or compressor, into the inflow (bottom) end of the Loflow meter. This meter must be arranged vertically using the spirit-level, so you will find it easier to place the air blower on the floor and run its outflow pipe up to the Loflow meter.

Plug the vacuum cleaner or compressor, via its speed controller, into the mains supply but do not switch on yet.

Set the 'temperature adjust' control to around the middle of its range and then connect up the anemometer control box, battery, voltmeter and bulb filament (the anemometer filament) as shown in Figure 3.6.

Look down the open end of the tube and turn the 'temperature adjust' control until the filament just begins to glow, then quickly turn it back slightly so that it just stops glowing.

? Why must the filament not be allowed to glow for long?

It would quickly oxidize in the air and burn out.

Draw up a table for your results like Table 3.2.

voltmeter reading/V	flow rate/ litre min^{-1}	flow rate/ m^3 min^{-1}	air speed/ m s^{-1}

Table 3.2
Table of results for Exploration 3.3

Switch on the vacuum cleaner or compressor and record the voltmeter reading and (i) flow of air in 1 minute with the British Gas laboratory gas meter, or (ii) the flow rate in litre min^{-1} with the Loflow meter, for a broad range of flow rates. (*Note:* The maximum flow rate through the laboratory gas meter must not exceed 42 litre min^{-1}. The Loflow meter LF3050E has a range of 5–50 litre min^{-1} and the LF3135E a range of 20–135 litre min^{-1}.) Switch off when you have taken all your readings and also disconnect the leads to the 6 V battery.

Remembering that 1 litre is 10^{-3} m^3, fill in the values of the flow rate in cubic metres per second.

Measure and record the internal diameter of the pipe through which the air flows.

Now calculate the air speeds from the expression

$$\text{air speed} = \frac{\text{flow rate}}{\text{cross-sectional area of tube}} \tag{3.1}$$

This expression is easily derived as follows.

Let the cross-sectional area of the tube be A and let the air be travelling at speed v. In a time t the air will have travelled a distance vt and occupies a volume of Avt. (See Figure 3.7.)

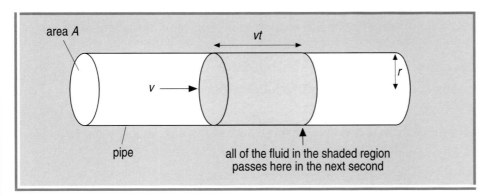

Figure 3.7 Detail of tube with air flowing through it

The flow rate is the volume of air that passes through each second, hence

$$\text{flow rate} = \frac{Avt}{t}$$
$$= Av$$

or in words

$$\text{flow rate} = \text{cross-sectional area of the tube} \times \text{air speed}$$

Rearranging we have

$$\text{air speed} = \frac{\text{flow rate}}{\text{cross-sectional area of tube}} \qquad \text{(Equation 3.1)}$$

Remember that cross-sectional area = $\pi \times$ (radius of tube)^2. Do ensure that the cross-sectional area is in m^2 and the flow rate in m^{3}s^{-1} in order to obtain an air speed in m s^{-1}.

Plot a graph of voltmeter reading (on the y-axis) against the air speed (on the x-axis). You now have the hot-wire anemometer calibrated for further use.

Q5 Is there a linear relationship between the air speeds and the voltmeter readings? ◆

◆E Exploration 3.4 Using a hot-wire anemometer

40 MINUTES

Apparatus:

◆ as for Exploration 3.3, with ◆ portable bulb holder

Carefully remove the bulb from the tube, remount it in the portable holder and connect this up to the control box. Use this portable system to investigate one or more of the following.

(i)   Air speeds around your college or school buildings.

(ii)   Air intake speeds at different settings of a fume cupboard.

(iii) The air speed of a fan.

(iii) Air speeds at different distances away from a hedge.

(iv) Air speeds at different heights close to a hedge.

(v)   Air speeds around a car parked on open ground in a breeze.

(vi) Air speeds around model aircraft, model cars or model buildings placed in a breeze or in a wind tunnel.

If you have time, you can continue learning about hot-wire anemometers by doing Exploration 3.5. The purpose is to see how the temperature of the filament affects the system's sensitivity.

◆E Exploration 3.5 Does the filament's temperature have an effect?

15 MINUTES

Apparatus:

◆ as for Exploration 3.3

Turn the 'temperature adjust' control to make the filament cooler and again obtain readings that would enable you to plot a graph of air speed against voltmeter reading. Plot the graph.

Q6 How does making the filament cooler affect the sensitivity of this system? ◆

Q7 A hot-wire anemometer could be operated under 'constant current' conditions, keeping the current through the filament the same all the time. What problem might arise at low speeds using this technique? ◆

Q8 This open filament is subject to contamination by dust in the airstream. Explain how this might affect its operation. ◆

Q9 What might be the best way of orienting the filament relative to the airstream in order to minimize contamination by dust? ◆

Q10 The set of results in Table 3.3 was obtained from a hot-wire anemometer exploration.

Table 3.3

Air speed/m s^{-1}	Voltmeter reading/V
0.00	2.62
0.21	2.73
0.42	2.79
0.61	2.83
0.81	2.87
1.05	2.91

(a) Plot a graph of air speed against voltmeter reading.

(b) From your graph, would it be true to say that the air speed is directly proportional to the voltmeter reading? Explain. ◆

3.2 Measuring chemical, oil and gas flow

You may know that when water flows slowly through an instant shower it heats up more than when it flows through quickly. (Some of you may have learnt this through experience when someone else turned on another tap while you were having shower!) This idea forms the basis of another technique for measuring flow rates, which depends on heating the fluid concerned, measuring the temperature rise brought about, and relating this to the rate of flow. It is used commercially, particularly in chemical, oil and gas industries, to indicate and control rates of flow. When air flows over a heated resistor, energy is continuously transferred to the surrounding air. The air gets hotter by an amount dependent on the rate of air flow and the power delivered to the resistor. Hence the change of temperature of the flowing air, before and after heating at a fixed rate, will provide a measure of the rate of flow. The technique is used for both liquids and gases.

Exploration 3.6 enables you to model this technique.

E Exploration 3.6
Using a heater and thermometers to measure air flow rates

Apparatus:

◆ heating tube (mounted on a board) ◆ two matched thermometers, −10°C to +50°C in 0.5°C steps, or two temperature probes ◆ 0–12 V d.c. power supply
◆ variable resistor/rheostat, 10–50 W (if not already incorporated into power supply)
◆ ammeter, 0–5 A d.c. ◆ voltmeter, 0–10 V d.c. ◆ cylinder vacuum cleaner or air compressor ◆ variac or drill speed controller ◆ connecting tubes and bungs
◆ stopwatch (for British Gas laboratory gas meter only) ◆ spirit-level (for Loflow meters only) ◆ leads ◆ heavy slotted base (Griffin and George STA-395-W)
◆ calibrated air flow meter (British Gas laboratory gas meter or Loflow meters Griffin and George FJC-700-100D and FJC-700-110A)

Place the board holding the pipe assembly, thermometers and power resistor into the heavy slotted base.

If you are using a British Gas laboratory gas meter, connect its outflow into the pipe's left-hand end, keeping the connecting tubing as straight and short as possible. If you are using a Loflow meter, connect its outflow end (top) into the pipe's left-hand end, bending the connecting tubing as little as possible. Figure 3.8 shows the experimental set-up.

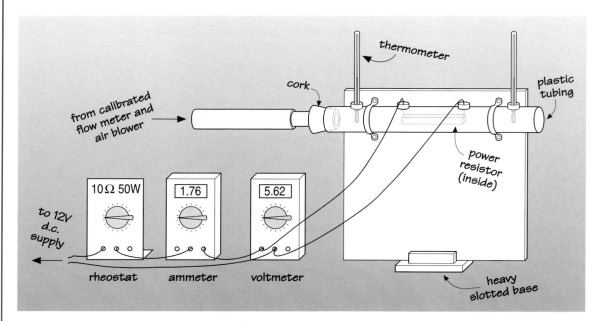

Figure 3.8 Experimental set-up for Exploration 3.6

Connect the outflow from the vacuum cleaner (blow end), or compressor, into the British Gas laboratory gas meter's input. Again, keep the piping as straight and short as possible. Or connect the outflow from the vacuum cleaner (blow end), or compressor, into the inflow (bottom) end of the Loflow meter. This meter must be arranged vertically using the spirit-level, so you will find it easier to place the air blower on the floor and run its outflow pipe up to the Loflow meter.

Plug the vacuum cleaner or compressor, via its speed controller, into the mains supply but do not switch on yet.

Connect up the circuit as shown in Figure 3.8, but do not switch on anything yet.

Draw up a table like Table 3.4 to record your results.

flow rate/litre min^{-1}	temperature/°C

Table 3.4
Table of results for Exploration 3.6

Switch on the power supply and adjust it (or the variable resistor/rheostat) until the power delivered to the resistor ($P = VI$) in the heating tube is between 6 and 9 W. The precise value is not important.

Switch on the vacuum cleaner or compressor and adjust the air flow to a fairly slow rate of between 7 and 10 litre min^{-1}. Leave the system running until the temperature readings stabilize – this will take some time.

Obtain a range of temperature readings by using different air flow rates, allowing the temperatures to stabilize each time before noting the readings in the table.

Calculate the changes in temperature and record them in the table.

Plot a graph of flow of air in one minute against the change in temperature. Your graph is a calibration graph for this particular heating tube being used as a flow rate measuring device.

Q11 Is the change of temperature inversely proportional to the flow of air in one minute? ◆

Now that you have seen this effect and taken some measurements, it is time to look a little more closely at the physics involved in this energy transfer.

The amount by which substances rise in temperature depends on the amount of energy transferred, their mass and their **specific heat capacity**. In your earlier science course you probably did an experiment that involved heating some water and, separately, a block of aluminium for ten minutes or so using a small immersion heater.

 If an immersion heater is rated at 50 W and is switched on for 10 minutes, how much energy has been transferred by it?

Energy transferred = power × time of transfer

$$= 50\,\text{W} \times (10 \times 60)\,\text{s}$$

$$= 30\,000\,\text{J}$$

 Using the expression

energy transferred = mass × specific heat capacity × temperature rise

calculate the temperature rise of 1.0 kg of water in 10 minutes after being heated by this same immersion heater. The specific heat capacity of water over this temperature range is $4200\,\text{J kg}^{-1}\,°\text{C}^{-1}$.

Energy transferred $= 30\,000\,\text{J}$

$$= 1.0\,\text{kg} \times 4200\,\text{J kg}^{-1}\,°\text{C}^{-1} \times \text{temperature rise}$$

so

$$\text{temperature rise} = \frac{30\,000\,\text{J}}{1.0\,\text{kg} \times 4200\,\text{J kg}^{-1}\,°\text{C}^{-1}}$$

$$= 7.1°\text{C (to two significant figures)}$$

 In reality, the water will not get this hot. Why not?

Some of the energy transferred will heat the containing vessel, some will heat the thermometer and some will go into the surroundings and heat the air.

Q12 If 1.00 kg of air of specific heat capacity $993\,\text{J kg}^{-1}\,\text{K}^{-1}$ flowed past a heater of power rating 100 W in exactly 2 minutes, (a) what, in theory, is the most that the air would heat up by, and (b) why, in practice, would it not heat up by quite this amount? ◆

Q13 The data shown in Table 3.5 were collected in an experiment investigating change of temperature with various flow rates of air.

Table 3.5 Data for Question 13

Flow of air in 1 minute/litre min^{-1}	Change of temperature/°C
7.2	24.0
11.2	20.0
16.6	17.0
22.2	16.0
27.5	15.5
34.8	15.0

(a) Plot a graph of flow of air in 1 minute against change in temperature.

(b) If the change in temperature was 21°C, what was the flow of air in 1 minute?

(c) How would you summarize the tendency of the temperature to change as the flow of air gets faster? ◆

E **Exploration 3.7 Using a heater and electronic temperature sensors to measure air flow rates**

50 MINUTES

Apparatus:

◆ as for Exploration 3.6 except instead of the two thermometers ◆ two temperature sensing integrated circuits, such as the LM35DZ (RS 317-960) ◆ differential amplifier ◆ computer datalogger

Each temperature sensing integrated circuit has an output of 10 mV °C^{-1} and is designed to give 0 V output at 0°C. Two of these could replace the traditional thermometers in Exploration 3.6, with their outputs fed into a differential amplifier. The temperature difference would then be indicated by the amplifier's output, a difference between the two sensors of 10°C resulting in an output of 0.1 V. If you connect them to a computer datalogger you will see how the temperatures change from switch-on or the effect of changing the flow rate or the power input.

An advantage of using electronic sensors is that it becomes easier to develop the set-up into a control system where the output of the amplifier is fed back to control the speed of flow. In this way you can set the flow rate to the desired level and then the system will automatically maintain it.

3.3 Using pressure to measure fluid flow

In some situations a measure of the difference in pressure between two points is used to calculate the speed of fluid flow. If you have completed Exploration 2.1 in Section 2 you will have already made this kind of measurement.

The speeds of fluids that are not too viscous and are flowing through pipes can be measured using a **venturimeter**. This meter is a straightforward device, it is basically a tube with a constriction in it, but to understand how it is used you will need to gain an appreciation of ideas that Bernoulli developed. We will now lead you through these.

Measuring pressures

A mercury barometer

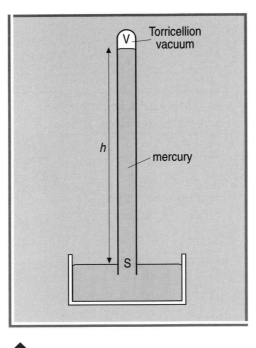

Figure 3.9
Schematic diagram of a mercury barometer

You may well have measured atmospheric pressure using a mercury barometer (see Figure 3.9), finding the height of the mercury column above the reservoir to be around 0.76 m. But how can you calculate the pressure in N m^{-2} or Pa (pascal) from this? (The vacuum above the mercury is named after the Italian scientist Evangelista Torricelli (1608–47) who made the first barometer in 1643.)

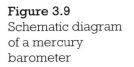 What is the pressure in the Torricellian vacuum V above the mercury column?

Zero, if it is a vacuum. That is what a vacuum means – no pressure at all because of the absence of any molecules moving about in that space. In reality it is not quite so, because there is vapour pressure due to some mercury having vaporized. However, at 20°C this amounts to the equivalent of just 0.01 mm of mercury pressure.

The pressure at the surface of the mercury open to the air is atmospheric pressure, therefore the pressure at point S inside the glass tube is also atmospheric: as the pressure in any liquid is the same at the same level.

As the pressure at V is zero, the difference in pressure between S and V is atmospheric pressure minus zero – just atmospheric pressure.

We can use this idea to formulate a very useful equation for pressure due to a column of fluid. We will write the density of mercury as $\rho_{mercury}$ and the cross-sectional area of the tube as A.

So, the volume of mercury above S is Ah, and the mass of this mercury is $\rho_{mercury} Ah$. The weight of this mass is $\rho_{mercury}gAh$, so the pressure at S due to the column of mercury above it is

$$P = \frac{\rho_{mercury}\,gAh}{A}$$

$$= \rho_{mercury}\,gh$$

As this column could be any fluid, we can turn this equation into a general expression by writing it as

$$P = \rho gh$$

(*Note:* This expression is independent of the cross-sectional area of the tube, which makes it more useful.)

 The atmosphere exerts a pressure of 1.0×10^5 Pa and the density of air is 1.2 kg m^{-3}. Using $g = 10$ N kg^{-1}, calculate the height of the atmosphere using the equation $P = \rho gh$. Considering how you arrived at your answer, what can you say about it?

$P = \rho gh$

therefore

$$h = \frac{P}{\rho g}$$

$$= \frac{1.0 \times 10^5 \, \text{Pa}}{1.2 \, \text{kg m}^{-3} \times 10 \, \text{N kg}^{-1}}$$

$$= 8.3 \times 10^3 \, \text{m}$$

$$= 8.3 \, \text{km}$$

This is a very low value for the thickness of the atmosphere – if it were correct it would mean that the top of Mount Everest is virtually in space. We have assumed that both the density of air and Earth's gravitational field remain constant, whereas we know that they do not. We can therefore say that we are confident that the Earth's atmosphere extends to more than 8.3 km.

Q14 As mentioned earlier, atmospheric pressure is approximately the pressure that will support a column of mercury 0.76 m high. What is this pressure in N m^{-2} or Pa? Mercury has a density $\rho_{mercury} = 1.36 \times 10^4$ kg m^{-3} and $g = 9.81$ N kg^{-1}. ◆

Now that you have become familiar with using the height of a fluid to find a pressure difference, we can think about how this can then be used to measure flow rates. Our next step is to look at another instrument that measures pressure difference – the **manometer**. You may well have used a giant manometer when doing work on lungs in earlier years.

A manometer is simply a tube curved into a U that contains a liquid, often just coloured water. A manometer is shown in Figure 3.10 – the pressure P_1 is higher than the pressure P_2 and has pushed the water until the pressure produced by the column h balances the pressure difference $P_1 - P_2$.

We can ignore the pressures produced by the water below L, as it is the same each side. This means that we have the same situation as we had for the mercury barometer.

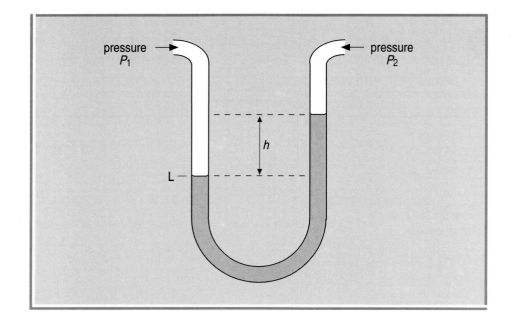

Figure 3.10
A U-tube
manometer

Q15 A U-tube manometer contains a liquid of density 784 kg m^{-3} and shows a difference in levels of 15 cm. If $g = 9.81$ N kg^{-1}, what pressure difference produced this? ◆

Q16 Why would mercury of density 1.36×10^4 kg m^{-3} not be a sensible liquid to use in a manometer to measure low pressures? ◆

Exploration 3.8 makes use of a manometer to measure pressure. In fact, we are measuring a difference in pressure. In this case it is the difference between the pressure of the gas supply and that of the atmosphere.

Exploration 3.8
Measuring the pressure of a gas supply

10 MINUTES

Apparatus:

◆ U-tube manometer half-filled with coloured water ◆ heavy slotted base (Griffin and George STA-395-W) ◆ ruler ◆ spirit-level ◆ protractor ◆ access to gas supply

Part (i)

Fit the U-tube manometer into the heavy slotted base and check that it is vertical. Connect the U-tube manometer to the gas supply and turn on the stopcock.

Measure the difference in levels and calculate the pressure difference. Take the density of water as 1000 kg m^{-3} and $g = 9.81 \text{ N kg}^{-1}$.

Part (ii)

Note what happens to the difference in levels (as measured along the tube) when the manometer is tilted through an angle of 60° to the left or right so that it forms an angle of 30° to the horizontal, as in Figure 3.11.

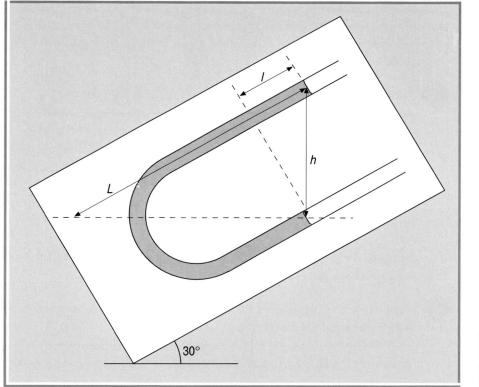

Figure 3.11
Finding h when the manometer is at an angle

Q17 Explain why you obtain this particular new difference in levels. ◆

Q18 What might be a sensible thing to do in order to measure very low pressure differences with a U-tube manometer? ◆

Q19 A U-tube manometer is tilted so that it is at an angle of 15.0° to the horizontal. It contains a liquid of density 784 kg m^{-3} and $g = 9.81$ N kg^{-1}. If it registers a difference in levels (as measured along the tubes) of 8.20 cm, what pressure difference is being detected? ◆

Transfer efficiency

Fluid fuels such as oil and gas are often transported large distances through pipelines. Energy is needed to do this. The **transfer efficiency** of transporting fluids in pipelines is calculated from the equation

$$\text{transfer efficiency} = \frac{\text{energy needed to transfer the fluid}}{\text{energy that is stored in the fluid}}$$

We need to take care when discussing transfer efficiencies. We usually use the term 'energy transfer' when we talk about energy changing from one form to another – from chemical potential energy to thermal energy, for example. And when we speak of efficiencies we usually quote them in terms of percentages, where an efficiency of 100% means that all the energy has been transferred successfully without loss or waste. However, when we say 'transfer efficiency' we are not talking about transferring energy between forms but about the energy cost of transporting a fuel. A transfer efficiency of 1 means that the energy needed to move the fuel from one place to another is the same as the energy stored in the fuel. This is the break-even point.

 Should we aim for large or small transfer efficiencies?

The smaller the better, as this means that less energy is used to transport the same amount of fuel. (This is unusual as we normally express efficiencies in percentages where the higher the percentage the more efficient the process.) We would usually avoid values of 1 and above – we don't want a transport system where more energy is required to transfer the fuel than is contained by the fuel itself!

The pressure drop ΔP across the ends of a pipe can be used to measure how efficiently a fluid is being transferred through the pipe.

 Write down a formula for the energy needed to transport one cubic metre of liquid along the pipe.

The energy required to transfer volume V with pressure drop ΔP is

$$\Delta E = V \Delta P \tag{3.2}$$

So, the energy needed per unit volume is

$$\frac{\Delta E}{V} = \frac{V \Delta P}{V}$$
$$= \Delta P$$

72

The amount of energy available from a cubic metre of fuel is called its **energy density**, U. The transfer efficiency for liquids can be usefully expressed as

$$\text{transfer efficiency} = \frac{\Delta P}{U}$$

where ΔP is the pressure drop across the pipe (Pa) and U is the energy density of the liquid (J m^{-3})

Q20 Crude oil has an energy density of about 3.50×10^{10} J m^{-3}. It is pumped down a 500 km pipeline with a transfer efficiency of 5.00×10^{-4}.

(a) Calculate the pressure drop from one end of the pipeline to the other.

(b) Atmospheric pressure is about 100 kPa. If the oil arrives at atmospheric pressure, how many atmospheres must it be at the other end?

(c) In practice, the pipeline has pumps at intervals of 10 km along its length. If the oil arrives at each pump at atmospheric pressure, at what pressure must the oil leave the pump?

(d) By considering your answers to (b) and (c), suggest why many small pumps along the length of the pipeline are used rather than a single large one at the start. ◆

The calculations you have just done were for the transfer of liquids, which are incompressible. Their volume hardly changes as their pressure is changed. So the volume of liquid that enters one end of a pipe is virtually the same as the volume that comes out of the other end.

Gases, however, are different. Their volume decreases as the pressure increases. Most gases obey the ideal gas equation quite well:

$$PV = nRT$$

where P is the pressure of the gas, V its volume, n the number of moles of the gas, R the gas constant (8.31 J mol^{-1} K^{-1}) and T the temperature (in kelvin).

 How does the volume of some gas flowing into a pipe compare with the volume flowing out the other end?

The pressure drops as the gas flows through, so its volume increases.

However, for both types of fluid, the mass flow rate is the same at both ends of a pipe and the number of molecules entering the pipe must equal the number leaving the other end.

Equation (3.2) is very straightforward to use when calculating the work done forcing a gas through a pipe and gives good results as long as the size of the pressure drop ΔP is very small compared with the initial pressure of the fluid: i.e. $\Delta P \ll P$.

When the pressure drop is significant with respect to the pressure, we have to use a modified equation, which we give here for completeness.

$$\Delta E = P_f V_f \ln\left(\frac{P_i}{P_f}\right) \tag{3.3}$$

where ΔE is the work done on the gas, P_i is the initial pressure of the gas, P_f is the final pressure of the gas, V_f is the final volume of the gas and

$\ln\left(\dfrac{P_i}{P_f}\right)$ means take the natural logarithm of $\left(\dfrac{P_i}{P_f}\right)$

If you are not familiar with this mathematical function, look for a button marked 'ln' among the functions on your calculator. It may be close to or combined with another function marked 'log' (this is also a logarithm but will give different values, so be careful which you use).

Q21 Methane (natural gas) is delivered around the country by a network of pipes. The energy density of methane at 120 kPa is about $2 \times 10^7 \, \mathrm{J \, m^{-3}}$. Assume that methane enters the network of pipes at a pressure of 120 kPa and emerges at a pressure of 105 kPa.

(a) Use Equations (3.2) and (3.3) to find the energy required to deliver each cubic metre of gas through the pipe.

(b) Calculate the transfer efficiency of this system. ◆

◆ **Exploration 3.9**
Exploring pressures in a fluid flow system

50 MINUTES

Apparatus:
◆ four 50 cm lengths of 5 mm diameter glass tubing ◆ clamps, stands and bosses ◆ four glass T-pieces ◆ five 10 cm lengths of 1 mm internal diameter glass capillary tubing (neither length nor diameter are critical, but the pieces must be the same as each other) ◆ an empty plastic bottle with the base cut off (a fizzy drink bottle is ideal) ◆ a ring clamp to hold the bottle ◆ a bung pierced with a short length of glass tubing to fit the neck of the bottle ◆ twelve pieces of rubber tubing to fix the glass tubes to the T-pieces ◆ one longer piece of rubber tubing to connect a T-piece to the bung ◆ a 50 cm rule ◆ plastic beakers to catch the water and fill the bottle

Figure 3.12 illustrates some apparatus that can be used to explore the variation of pressure in water as it flows down a pipe. The height of the water column in each vertical glass tube is a measure of the water pressure at the base of that tube. Where will the pressure be greatest? Where will it be least? Which capillary tube will need the greatest pressure drop?

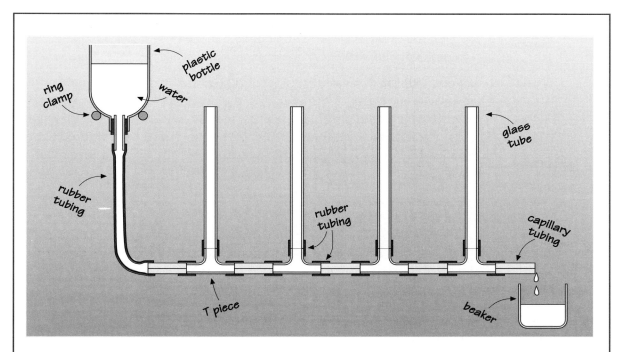

Figure 3.12 Equipment for exploring pressures in a fluid flow system

Arrange the apparatus as shown in Figure 3.12. The glass tubes must be supported vertically and be at the same level.

Fill the bottle with water. The top surface of the water in the bottle should be about 50 cm above the capillary tubes. You may have to tap on the glass with a finger to encourage bubbles of air trapped in the T-pieces to rise to the top of the glass tubes.

When conditions are steady, measure the height of the water columns in each glass tube. (You need the distance from the top surface of the water to the centre of the capillary tubes.)

Calculate the pressure drop across each length of capillary tubing. (The density of water is 10^3 kg m^{-3}.) Is it the same every time? Why might that be so?

Repeat the experiment for different heights of water in the bottle.

Bernoulli's equation

When a fluid flows from a wide tube to a narrower one, the speed of flow changes. This change of speed is caused by a change in pressure. If you know what this change of pressure is, it is possible to calculate the change of speed. The theoretical basis behind this was first developed by the Swiss physicist and mathematician Daniel Bernoulli (1700–82) in his 1738 publication on fluid dynamics called *Hydrodynamica*. This section will take you through the development of what is today called Bernoulli's equation. It is quite a lengthy argument, but it is not that difficult.

(*Note:* When you are confronted with a section like this, you will find it helpful to read it through several times. This way you will gradually become familiar with it and fully understand what is happening.)

Figure 3.13 shows a fluid passing along a horizontal pipe that narrows from area A_1 to area A_2. In doing so, the fluid accelerates from speed v_1 to speed v_2. As the pipe is horizontal, we can ignore the effects of gravity. It is the pressure difference between the ends that causes the fluid to accelerate. For v_2 to be greater than v_1 the pressure P_1 must be greater than P_2.

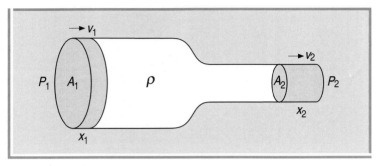

Figure 3.13
Fluid pressures and speeds in a wide tube that feeds into a narrow tube

Let the density ρ of the fluid remain constant. This is almost true, even for air, as long as the pressure difference is not too great.

Using

$$\text{pressure} = \frac{\text{force applied}}{\text{area of application}}$$

we can write an expression for the force F_1 exerted on the left-hand end by the pressure P_1 on an area A_1 by rearranging this equation to

$$\text{force applied} = \text{pressure} \times \text{area of application}$$

Replacing the words with symbols gives

$$F_1 = P_1 \times A_1 \tag{3.4}$$

In a time Δt the fluid at this input end is displaced a distance we can call x_1. Using

$$\text{work done} = \text{force applied}$$
$$\times \text{displacement in the direction of the force}$$

we can write an expression for the work done, W_1, by force F_1:

$$W_1 = F_1 x_1$$

From Equation (3.4), we can replace F_1 with $P_1 A_1$ to give

$$W_1 = P_1 A_1 x_1$$

 Write the equation for the work done, W_2, in moving the fluid in the narrow part of the tube for the same time.

$$W_2 = F_2 x_2$$
$$= -P_2 A_2 x_2$$

(*Note:* We have included a minus sign because the fluid is moving against the pressure P_2, as P_1 is larger and is producing the motion.)

We can now write an expression for the total work done in moving fluid in this section of pipe.

$$W = W_1 + W_2$$
$$= P_1 A_1 x_1 - P_2 A_2 x_2 \qquad (3.5)$$

To reduce and simplify this we need to write it in terms of something that doesn't change from the wide tube to the narrow tube in this time.

> If the fluid is incompressible, what property of the fluid that has moved in either region has not changed?

Look at the shaded sections in Figure 3.13. These have different areas and different lengths but their volumes are identical. Also, as we have assumed that density is constant, the mass of fluid will also be the same.

Let's put this in terms of mass to make it easier and form expressions for the mass of fluid in each region of tubing. We begin by finding the volume

$$V_1 = A_1 x_1$$

Now, you should remember that

$$\text{density} = \frac{\text{mass}}{\text{volume}}$$

giving

$$m_1 = \rho V_1$$
$$= \rho A_1 x_1$$

and (as $m = m_1 = m_2$)

$$m = \rho A_1 x_1 = \rho A_2 x_2 \qquad (3.6)$$

We won't try to combine this equation with our one for the work done (Equation 3.5) as mass does not appear in it. We will incorporate it into one for kinetic energy as this will be more straightforward.

From the equation for kinetic energy

$$E_k = \frac{1}{2}mv^2$$

kinetic energy of $m_1 = \frac{1}{2}m_1v_1^2$

and we can replace m_1 with $\rho A_1 x_1$ from Equation (3.6) giving

kinetic energy of $m_1 = \rho A_1 x_1 v_1^2$

and also therefore

kinetic energy of $m_2 = \rho A_1 x_1 v_2^2$

Earlier we found an expression for the work done on the fluid (Equation 3.5). If we assume that there are no losses, then all of the work done will go to increasing the fluid's kinetic energy.

 What losses could there be?

Some of the work done could go into heating the fluid through the resistive forces within the fluid itself (viscosity) and through friction with the pipe wall.

The change in kinetic energy is given by

$$\Delta E_k = E_{k1} - E_{k2}$$

$$= \frac{1}{2}\rho A_2 x_2 v_2^2 - \frac{1}{2}\rho A_1 x_1 v_1^2$$

and as this is equal to the work done given in Equation (3.5) we can write

$$P_1 A_1 x_1 - P_2 A_2 x_2 = \frac{1}{2}\rho A_2 x_2 v_2^2 - \frac{1}{2}\rho A_1 x_1 v_1^2 \qquad (3.7)$$

We can simplify this right away. You will remember that we decided that the volume and the mass do not change as this fluid is incompressible.

Volume $= A_1 x_1 = A_2 x_2$

and

mass $= \rho A_1 x_1 = \rho A_2 x_2$ (Equation 3.6)

By making these two substitutions into Equation (3.7) we end up with

$$\left(P_1 - P_2\right)A_2 x_2 = \left(v_2^2 - v_1^2\right)\frac{1}{2}\rho A_2 x_2$$

Now, by dividing through by $A_2 x_2$ we get

$$P_1 - P_2 = \frac{1}{2}\rho\left(v_2^2 - v_1^2\right)$$

You may often see this expression arranged as

$$P_1 + \frac{1}{2}\rho v_1^2 = P_2 + \frac{1}{2}\rho v_2^2$$

This equation then links the pressures and the speeds in our two regions of pipe as long as the fluid is incompressible and there are no losses.

In more complicated cases, like the one shown in Figure 3.14, where there is a change of speed and height, there are transfers of both kinetic energy and gravitational potential energy and the expression becomes

$$P_1 + \frac{1}{2}\rho v_1^2 + \rho g h_1 = P_2 + \frac{1}{2}\rho v_2^2 + \rho g h_2$$

where h_1 and h_2 are the heights of the centres of the fluid sections above an arbitrary fixed point, as shown in Figure 3.14.

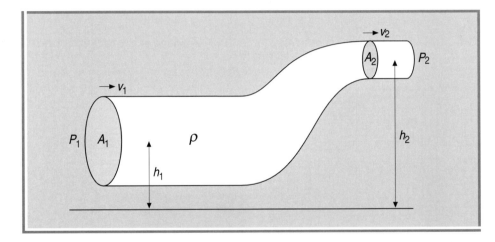

Figure 3.14
Fluid pressures and speeds in a wide tube that feeds into a narrow tube with a change of height

In general terms this expression is written as

$$P + \frac{1}{2}\rho v^2 + \rho g h = \text{constant} \qquad (3.8)$$

and is known as Bernoulli's equation. $P + \rho g h$ is known as the 'static pressure' and $\frac{1}{2}\rho v^2$ is known as the 'dynamic pressure'. From this we can say that the total pressure is constant and is the sum of the static pressure and the dynamic pressure.

◆ **E** ▶ Exploration 3.10 Measuring air speed with a venturimeter

Apparatus:

◆ venturimeter assembly mounted on a board ◆ graph paper grid ◆ cylinder vacuum cleaner or air compressor ◆ variac or drill speed controller ◆ vernier microscope (if required) ◆ spirit-level ◆ connecting tubing ◆ stopwatch (for British Gas laboratory gas meter only) ◆ heavy slotted base (Griffin and George STA-395-W) ◆ calibrated air flow meter (British Gas laboratory gas meter or Loflow meters Griffin and George FJC-700-100D and FJC-700-110A)

To investigate what happens in a venturimeter and see how it can be used to measure the speed of flow of air you will use a tube with a constriction, or narrowing, in it called a venturi. It is named after Giovanni Battista Venturi (1746–1822) who outlined its principle of operation. When a venturi is being used to measure speeds, it is referred to as a venturimeter.

Place the board holding the venturimeter assembly (which consists of a venturi attached to a manometer – see Figure 3.15) into the heavy slotted base.

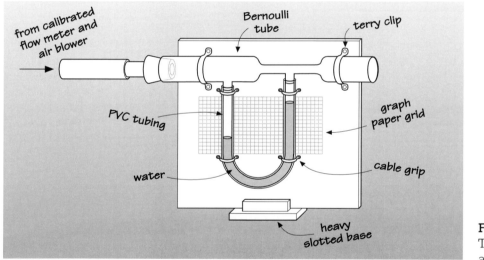

Figure 3.15
The venturimeter assembly

Adjust the board, using the spirit-level, until the glass tubing of the venturimeter is horizontal.

Connect the outflow from the British Gas laboratory gas meter into the pipe's left-hand end, keeping the connecting tubing as straight and as short as possible. Now connect the outflow from the vacuum cleaner or compressor into the British Gas laboratory gas meter's input. Again, it is important to keep the piping as straight and short as possible.

If you are using a Loflow meter, connect its outflow end (top) into the pipe's left-hand end, bending the connecting tubing as little as possible. Now connect the outflow from the vacuum cleaner or compressor into the meter's inflow (bottom) end. Remember that this meter must be arranged vertically (using the spirit-level), so it will be easier to place the compressor on the floor and run the pipe up to the meter.

Plug the vacuum cleaner or compressor, via its speed controller, into the mains supply but do not switch on yet.

Adjust the speed controller so that when the vacuum cleaner or compressor is switched on it runs at a fairly slow speed. Also note that the British Gas laboratory gas meter has a maximum flow rate of 42 litre min^{-1}. Switch on and adjust further until the manometer registers a few centimetres difference in levels. Measure this difference in levels, Δh, accurately using the graph paper grid and record it.

Measure and record the flow of air in 1 minute and then switch off the air blower.

Unless the internal diameters of the two sections of tubing are already provided, you will need to measure these with a vernier microscope. The narrow section is usually impossible to measure accurately unless a broken one is available. Note down the values obtained or provided.

Assuming that the Bernoulli equation applies in this case we can write

$$P_1 + \frac{1}{2}\rho_{air}v_1^2 = P_2 + \frac{1}{2}\rho_{air}v_2^2$$

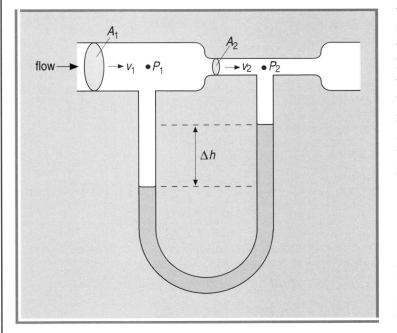

where ρ_{air} is the density of air, P_1 is the pressure in the wider tube above the left-hand manometer arm, P_2 is the pressure in the narrower tube above the right-hand manometer arm, v_1 is the speed of flow in the wider tube and v_2 is the speed of flow in the narrower tube (see Figure 3.16).

Figure 3.16
Schematic diagram of the pressures and flow speeds in the venturimeter

Since the volume of air passing through the wide and narrow tubes each second is assumed to be the same – the air not being compressed – we can write

$$v_1 A_1 = v_2 A_2$$

and so

$$v_2 = v_1 \frac{A_1}{A_2}$$

Substituting for v_2 in the Bernoulli equation we have

$$P_1 + \frac{1}{2}\rho_{air}v_1^2 = P_2 + \frac{1}{2}\rho_{air}\left(v_1\frac{A_1}{A_2}\right)^2$$

So

$$P_1 - P_2 = \frac{1}{2}\rho_{air}\left(v_1\frac{A_1}{A_2}\right)^2 - \frac{1}{2}\rho_{air}v_1^2$$

or

$$P_1 - P_2 = \frac{1}{2}\rho_{air}v_1^2\left(\frac{A_1^2}{A_2^2} - 1\right)$$

The difference of pressure $P_1 - P_2$ is calculated from $\rho_{water}g\Delta h$, where Δh is the difference in manometer levels, ρ_{water} is the density of the water in the manometer and g is the gravitational field strength. So we now have

$$\rho_{water}g\Delta h = \frac{1}{2}\rho_{air}v_1^2\left(\frac{A_1^2}{A_2^2} - 1\right)$$

Rearranging we have

$$v_1 = \sqrt{\frac{2\rho_{water}g\Delta h}{\rho_{air}\left(\dfrac{A_1^2}{A_2^2} - 1\right)}} \tag{3.9}$$

Use Equation (3.9) to calculate the speed of the air through the wider tube. At 20°C the density of water is approximately 998 kg m^{-3}, the density of air is around 1.2 kg m^{-3} at 20°C and the pressure likely in this section of the tube, and g is 9.81 N kg^{-1}.

Check how good the agreement is with the speed calculated from

$$\text{air speed} = \frac{\text{flow rate}}{\text{cross-sectional area of tube}} \tag{Equation 3.1}$$

where the cross-sectional area in question is A_1. (*Note:* Remember that 1 litre is 10^{-3} m^3.)

You will probably find that the agreement between the measured and calculated values of air speed is not very good. The reason for this is that Bernoulli's equation, upon which the calculations are based, applies strictly to streamlined, non-viscous, incompressible flow (streamlining and viscosity will be discussed in more detail in Section 4). In practice, a venturimeter needs to take account of the fact that even air is slightly viscous, there will be some turbulence caused by the joins of the wide and narrow tubes and that air is also compressible. This can be done by adding two factors to the final expression, both are empirical coefficients (found experimentally):

(i) C, the **coefficient of discharge**

(ii) ε, the **expansibility factor**.

The expression for a *real* gas then becomes

$$v_1 = C\varepsilon \sqrt{\frac{2\rho_{\text{water}}\, g\Delta h}{\rho_{\text{air}}\left(\dfrac{A_1^2}{A_2^2} - 1\right)}} \tag{3.10}$$

Using you own results, calculate a value for the product $C\varepsilon$. When you know this value you have calibrated your venturimeter (the value $C\varepsilon$ is sometimes known as the calibration coefficient). By using it in Equation (3.10) you can now calculate any other air speeds within its range of use.

Remove the British Gas laboratory gas meter or Loflow meter and directly connect the air blower to the venturimeter. Switch on and adjust its speed to the highest that the manometer can measure. Record the difference in heights of the liquid in the manometer arms. Switch off the air blower and calculate what this highest speed of use is.

Q22 Benzene of density 879 kg m^{-3} flows through a venturimeter. The inlet pipe has a diameter of 0.01 m and the throat diameter is 0.005 m. The water-filled manometer shows a height difference of 20 mm. If the coefficient of discharge, C, is 1 and the expansibility factor, ε, is also 1, calculate the speed of flow in the wider section. Use $\rho_{\text{water}} = 1000$ kg m^{-3} and $g = 9.8$ m s^{-2}. ◆

Q23 A venturimeter being used to measure the flow of petrol in a pipeline has an inlet diameter of 0.3 m and a throat diameter of 0.15 m. The height difference between the mercury in the two arms of the manometer is 73.9 mm and the density of the petrol is 780 kg m^{-3}. Take the coefficient of discharge, C, to be 0.98, the expansibility factor, ε, to be 1, the density of the mercury to be 13 800 kg m^{-3} and $g = 9.8$ m s^{-2}.

(a) What is the speed of flow of the petrol in the inlet pipe?

(b) What is the rate of flow in m^3 s^{-1} of the petrol? ◆

The venturi effect has been used in other applications. For example, venturis are used in a non-measuring capacity in some motor vehicles of older design. Here the lowering of pressure in the narrow section causes fuel to be *pushed* into a carburettor to mix with air prior to passing into an engine cylinder to be ignited (see Figure 3.17 overleaf).

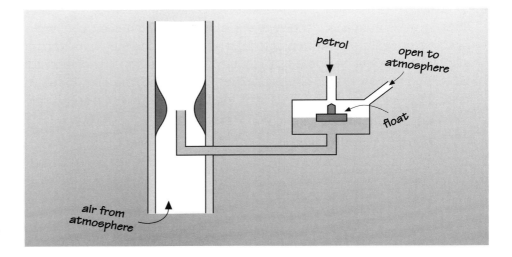

Figure 3.17
A venturi used in a carburettor

You will also be very familiar with another application: the Bunsen burner (see Figure 3.18). Perfume sprayers also make good use of the effect (see Figure 3.19).

Q24 Look at the diagram of the Bunsen burner in Figure 3.18.

(a) Gas coming in along the rubber tubing suddenly passes through a tiny jet. What will happen to the pressure in the vicinity of this jet at A?

(b) If the pressure of the air outside at B is greater than that at A, what will happen to the air outside? ◆

Q25 Explain the working of the old-fashioned perfume sprayer illustrated in the Figure 3.19. ◆

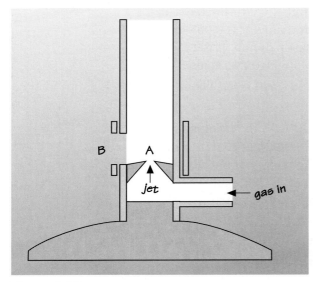

Figure 3.18
A Bunsen burner

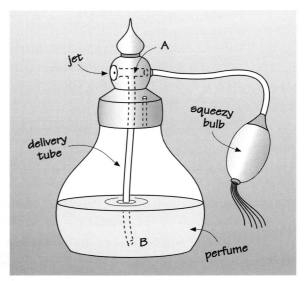

Figure 3.19
An old-fashioned perfume sprayer

Q26 The following results were obtained as air flowed through a venturimeter of wide tube internal diameter 9.70 mm and narrow tube internal diameter 5.15 mm:

> difference in water manometer levels = 8.00 cm
>
> density of water = 998 kg m^{-3}
>
> density of air = 1.2 kg m^{-3}
>
> g = 9.81 N kg^{-1}

(a) What was the pressure difference between the two sections of the venturimeter?

(b) Using the expression

$$v_1 = \sqrt{\dfrac{2\rho_{\text{water}}\,g\Delta h}{\rho_{\text{air}}\left(\dfrac{A_1^2}{A_2^2} - 1\right)}}$$

(Equation 3.9)

calculate the predicted air speed.

(c) If the speed of air flow as recorded by the calibrated flow meter was 8.80 m s^{-1}, calculate the calibration coefficient $C\varepsilon$ of this venturimeter. ◆

3.4 Measuring the relative speed of an aircraft

Pressure difference is also used to measure the speed of aircraft. As an aircraft travels, air, in effect, flows past it. The speed of the flow of air passing an aircraft is its relative speed, and a device that can measure this is the pitot tube. It is one of the oldest fluid speed meters and was invented by Henri Pitot (1695–1771) in 1732. Today, in the slightly modified form of the pitot-static tube (see Figure 3.20), it is very widely used to measure air speeds, particularly on aircraft.

The same device can also be used to measure liquid speeds, and an electronic version was designed by Michael Lord, while he was still a student, for a sailboard. He wrote an article for The Institution of Electrical Engineers' magazine for schools *Electronics Education* in Spring 1994. Read through the extract that we have reproduced overleaf. It is interesting to note that no one before him had thought of designing such a product for windsurfers.

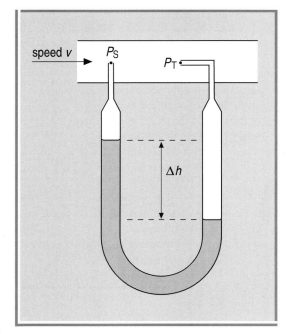

Figure 3.20
A pitot-static tube

PUPIL PROJECT
THE SPEED OF IT ALL

by Michael Lord

This invention arose from my own frustration at not being able to purchase a sailboard speedometer, as no reliable product was available. ...

My invention for measuring sailboard speed is, in essence, a specially designed replacement fin, as the fin is the common feature to all sailboards (Fig. 1). ...

The speedometer works by comparing the dynamic pressure generated by the movement of the board through the water with the static pressure which would be present at that point if the board were stationary.

It comprises a pressure sensitive comparator incorporating a force sensing transducer, moulded within a skeg [the fin], which produces a voltage output fed into an electronic circuit to give a readable display. The display unit is waterproof and mounted on the deck of the sailboard.

A pitot tube is used to create a dynamic pressure component generated by the flow. The tube fills with water and then acts on the transducer progressively, as the sailboard speed rises. The static tube, connected at right angles and open to the water on both sides of the skeg, allows the static pressure, which would be present if the board were at rest, to be determined. ...

The velocity value 'look up' tables in the memory chip have been calculated using Bernoulli's hypothesis, which relates velocity of a fluid to its dynamic and static pressures. ...

My prototype device has been programmed to cover a range of 0–25 knots which is sufficient for most recreational sailors' capabilities, but circuitry adjustments could easily enable the range to be varied as desired. ...

I believe that my device is unique and so I have submitted a patent application. The patent for the invention is now pending as the search by the Patent Office has not revealed any similar product. ...

Although the speedometer has received much interest, I have not yet obtained any firm commitments to its commercial exploitation. I am hopeful, though, that this remains a possibility.

(*Electronics Education*, Spring 1994)

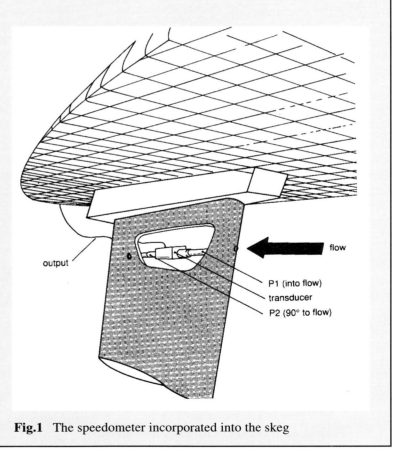

output
flow
P1 (into flow)
transducer
P2 (90° to flow)

Fig.1 The speedometer incorporated into the skeg

Michael Lord

Q27 A number of windsurfers can get their sailboards up to and over 20 knots (around 10 m s^{-1}). If Michael Lord's device was recording a pressure difference between the total pressure and static pressure of 32 800 N m^{-2}, how fast was the sailboard moving through the water? The density of sea water is 1025 kg m^{-3}. ◆

Q28 A pressure gauge measures the difference between the total pressure and the static pressure in a pitot-static tube mounted on the side of an aircraft. It shows a pressure difference of 1.0×10^4 N m^{-2}. At the height this aircraft is flying the density of the air is 0.5 kg m^{-3}. Calculate the speed of this aircraft through the air. ◆

A pitot-static tube measures the difference between the *total*, or *stagnation*, pressure on a small surface head-on to the flow, and the *static pressure* parallel to the flow. The difference between the two pressures provides a measure of the fluid speed. You will be using a pitot-static tube in Exploration 3.11, but first you need to read through a little theory.

Some theory

With no change in height of the moving fluid, the pitot-static tube is able to measure two pressures: the static pressure P_S above the left-hand manometer arm and the total pressure P_T at the head of the right-hand manometer arm (as shown in Figure 3.20 on p. 85). The total pressure is the sum of the static pressure and the dynamic pressure as given in Bernoulli's equation (Equation 3.8).

$$P + \frac{1}{2}\rho v^2 + \rho g h = \text{constant} \qquad \text{(Equation 3.8)}$$

where $P + \rho g h$ is the static pressure, P_S, and $\frac{1}{2}\rho v^2$ is the dynamic pressure. Hence we have

$$P_T = P_S + \frac{1}{2}\rho_{\text{air}} v^2$$

Rearranging we have

$$P_T - P_S = \frac{1}{2}\rho_{\text{air}} v^2$$

$P_T - P_S$ is measured directly from the difference in manometer levels.

Therefore

$$\frac{1}{2}\rho_{\text{air}} v^2 = \rho_{\text{water}} g \Delta h$$

Rearranging we have

$$v^2 = \frac{2\rho_{\text{water}} g \Delta h}{\rho_{\text{air}}}$$

and

$$v = \sqrt{\frac{2\rho_{\text{water}} g \Delta h}{\rho_{\text{air}}}} \qquad (3.11)$$

Now for the exploration itself.

E ▸ Exploration 3.11 Measuring air speed with a pitot-static tube

50 MINUTES

Apparatus:

- ◆ pitot-static tube assembly mounted on a board ◆ sheet of graph paper
- ◆ cylinder vacuum cleaner or air compressor ◆ variac or drill speed controller
- ◆ vernier microscope (if required) ◆ spirit-level ◆ connecting tubing
- ◆ stopwatch (for British Gas laboratory gas meter only) ◆ heavy slotted base (Griffin and George STA-395-W) ◆ calibrated air flow meter (British Gas laboratory gas meter or Loflow meters Griffin and George FJC-700-100D and FJC-700-110A)

Place the board holding the pitot-static tube assembly (which consists of a pitot-static tube attached to a manometer – see Figure 3.21) into the heavy slotted base.

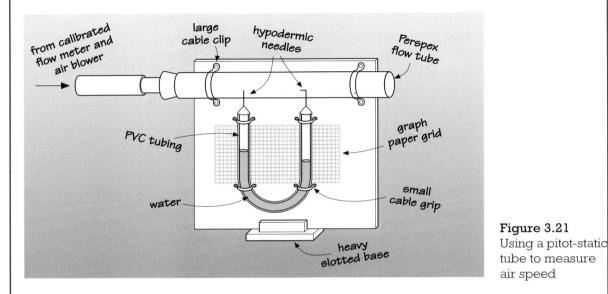

Figure 3.21
Using a pitot-static tube to measure air speed

Connect the outflow from the British Gas laboratory gas meter into the pipe's left-hand end, keeping the connecting tubing as straight and short as possible. Now connect the outflow from the vacuum cleaner or compressor into the British Gas laboratory gas meter's input. Again, it is important to keep the piping as straight and short as possible.

If you are using a Loflow meter, connect its outflow end (top) into the pipe's left-hand end, bending the connecting tubing as little as possible. Now connect the outflow from the vacuum cleaner or compressor into the meter's inflow (bottom) end. Remember that this meter must be arranged vertically (using the spirit-level), so it will be easier to place the compressor on the floor and run the pipe up to the meter.

Plug the vacuum cleaner or compressor, via its speed controller, into the mains supply but do not switch on yet.

Adjust the speed controller so that when the vacuum cleaner or compressor is switched on it runs at a fairly slow speed. Also note that the British Gas laboratory gas meter has a maximum flow rate of 42 litre min^{-1}. Switch on and adjust further until the manometer registers a difference in levels of about a centimetre. Measure this difference in levels, Δh, accurately using the graph paper grid and record it. Measure and record the flow of air in 1 minute and then switch off the air blower.

Unless the diameter of the flow pipe is already provided, you will need to measure this with a vernier microscope. Note down the value obtained or provided.

Use the expression

$$v = \sqrt{\frac{2\rho_{\text{water}} g \Delta h}{\rho_{\text{air}}}}$$
(Equation 3.11)

to calculate the speed of the air. At 20°C the density of water is approximately 998 kg m^{-3}, the density of air is around 1.2 kg m^{-3} at 20°C and the pressure likely in this section of the tube, and g is 9.81 N kg^{-1}. Do ensure that h is in metres.

Calculate the speed of the air and check how good the agreement is with the speed calculated from

$$\text{air speed} = \frac{\text{flow rate}}{\text{cross-sectional area of tube}}$$
(Equation 3.1)

which we derived earlier.

(*Note:* Remember that 1 litre is 10^{-3} m^3.)

You will probably find that the agreement between the measured and calculated values of air speed is not very good. The reason for this is that Bernoulli's equation, upon which the calculations are based, applies strictly to streamlined, non-viscous, incompressible flow (streamlining and viscosity will be discussed in more detail in Section 4). In practice, a pitot-static tube needs to take account of the fact that even air is slightly viscous, there will be some turbulence caused by the hypodermic needles and that air is also compressible. This can be done by adding two factors to the final expression, both are empirical coefficients (found experimentally): (i) C, the **coefficient of discharge**, (ii) ε, the **expansibility factor**.

The expression for a *real* gas then becomes

$$v = C\varepsilon \sqrt{\frac{2\rho_{\text{water}} g \Delta h}{\rho_{\text{air}}}}$$
(3.12)

From your own results, calculate a value for the product $C\varepsilon$. When you know this value you have calibrated your pitot-static tube (the value $C\varepsilon$ is sometimes known as the calibration coefficient). By using it in Equation (3.12) you can now calculate any other air speeds within its range of use.

Remove the British Gas laboratory gas meter or Loflow meter and directly connect the air blower to the pitot-static tube. Switch on and adjust its speed to the highest that the manometer can measure. Record the difference in heights of the liquid in the manometer arms. Switch off the air blower and calculate this highest speed of use.

Q29 A correction factor called the Mach factor has to be applied to the pitot-static tube expression $P_T - P_S = \frac{1}{2}\rho_{air}v^2$ when used with a supersonic aircraft travelling high up in the atmosphere. What do you think this Mach factor is likely to take into account? ◆

Q30 The manometer attached to a pitot-static tube shows a difference in levels of 9.0 mm. It contains water of density 998 kg m^{-3}. The density of air is 1.2 kg m^{-3}. The gravitational field strength g is 9.81 N kg^{-1}.

(a) Calculate the pressure difference shown by the manometer.

(b) Using the expression $v_{air} = \sqrt{\dfrac{2\rho_{water}g\Delta h}{\rho_{air}}}$ calculate the anticipated air speed.

(c) If a calibrated flow meter records an air speed of 8.8 m s^{-1}, what is the calibration coefficient $C\varepsilon$ for this pitot-static tube? ◆

Achievements

After working through this section you should be able to:

- calculate the pressure due to a column of liquid of known density

- calculate transfer efficiencies for flowing liquids

- explain why the volume of a gas increases as it flows from one place to another

- calculate the work required to transfer a volume of gas from one place to another

- explain that the pressure difference remains constant as a liquid flows down a pipe of fixed size

- describe the need for correction factors when calculating velocities of real gases from pressure differences.

Glossary

Average drift velocity The average speed of electrons moving through a wire when it is carrying a particular current.

Coefficient of discharge Symbol: C. A dimensionless constant that is found by experiment. It is added to the equation for the velocity of flow to make allowance for the real physical environment of this flow.

Differential amplifier A device whose input is two voltages and whose output is the voltage difference between these inputs.

Energy density The useful energy per unit volume of a fuel.

Expansibility factor Symbol: ε. A dimensionless constant whose value is found by experiment. It is used to modify equations to take into account the compressibility of real fluids.

Hot-wire anemometer A device that measures the speed of moving air by detecting the changing electrical resistance of a metallic conductor in the path of the air.

Manometer A piece of equipment used to measure pressure differences. It is a tube curved into a U shape containing a liquid.

Specific heat capacity The amount of heat required to raise unit mass of material by one unit of temperature. It is a property of the material. Usual units are $J\,kg^{-1}\,K^{-1}$.

Transfer efficiency The energy required to transfer a fuel divided by the energy that is stored in the fuel. Unusually for measures of efficiencies, the lower the value the better.

Venturimeter A meter used to measure the speeds of fluids flowing through pipes. It is basically a tube with a constriction in it connected to a device that can measure pressure differences, such as a manometer.

Answers to Ready to Study test

R1

(a)

$$I = \frac{V}{R}$$
$$= \frac{240\,V}{960\,\Omega}$$
$$= 0.25\,A$$

(b)

$$R = \frac{V}{I}$$
$$= \frac{12\,V}{2\,A}$$
$$= 6\,\Omega$$

R2

(a) The equation $V = IR$ is comparable to the equation for a straight line $y = mx + c$. We would expect a straight-line graph passing through the origin where the gradient of the line is the resistance R. Therefore, from $V = IR$ we expect that voltage is directly proportional to current when the resistance is fixed.

(b) A current passing through a resistance such as a wire will heat it. As the temperature of the resistance rises so too does its resistance, which will tend to decrease the current through it.

R3

(a) The resistance of the longer wire will be five times that of the shorter wire. The resistance is therefore $5 \times 12\ \text{W} = 60\ \text{W}$.

(b) When the wire is cut into four, each piece will have a quarter of the resistance of the original length, i.e.

$$\frac{12\,\Omega}{4} = 3\,\Omega$$

R4

$$E_k = \frac{1}{2}mv^2$$
$$= \frac{1}{2} \times 0.1\,\text{kg} \times \left(2\,\text{ms}^{-1}\right)^2$$
$$= 0.2\,\text{J}$$

Answers to questions in the text

Q1

$$R_1 = \frac{R_2 R_3}{R_4} = \frac{10\,\Omega \times 5\,\Omega}{25\,\Omega} = 2\,\Omega$$

Q2

It should be very linear.

Q3

Scraping the wire would make it thinner in some places than in others, which would mean that its resistance would not change linearly with length.

Q4

It should be quite linear.

Q5

No, it is not very linear, especially at the lower speeds.

Q6

Having a cooler filament lessens the sensitivity of the system – smaller changes of voltage are produced than before.

Q7

It may cause the filament to burn out. At the higher speeds energy would be transferred to the air quickly, so preventing the filament from getting too hot. At low speeds energy would be transferred at a low rate, so the filament would retain a lot of energy, get very hot, and quite likely burn out.

Q8

The dust may act as an insulator and prevent efficient energy transfer to the air. This would cause the filament to be hotter than anticipated and so, over time, the air speeds calculated from the calibration graph would diverge from the real values.

The dust may also partially short out some turns of the filament's coil, so altering its overall resistance from the value it had during calibration. This would affect the bridge voltage and consequently the heating of the filament itself. That in turn would produce results varying from those obtained when the system was first calibrated.

The nature of the dust present may well change the emissivity of the filament (the rate at which it can radiate energy). This would alter the filament's ability to transfer energy to the surroundings, and so again produce results different from those obtainable when it was first calibrated.

Q9

It is probably best for the axis of the filament coil to face in the same direction as the air flow. It will then offer a small target to the air stream and so collect less dust. It is also likely to stretch less in this orientation.

Q10

(a) See Figure 3.22.

(b) They are certainly not directly proportional to each other. If they were, the graph would have been a straight line passing through the origin. It is not. At the higher speeds the voltmeter readings appear to be quite linear; less so at lower speeds

Q11

No, it is not. To be inversely proportional the change in temperature would have to be halved when the flow rate was doubled.

Q12

(a) Energy transferred = power rating
$$\times \text{ time of heating}$$

So we have

$$\text{energy transferred} = 100\,\text{W} \times (2 \times 60)\,\text{s}$$
$$= 12\,000\,\text{J}$$

In heating a substance we use the expression

$$\text{energy transferred} = \text{mass}$$
$$\times \text{ specific heat capacity}$$
$$\times \text{ temperature rise}$$

and so we have

$$12\,000\,\text{J} = 1.00\,\text{kg} \times 993\,\text{J}\,\text{kg}^{-1}\,\text{K}^{-1}$$
$$\times \text{ temperature rise}$$

Therefore

$$\text{temperature rise} = \frac{12\,000\,\text{J}}{1.00\,\text{kg} \times 993\,\text{J}\,\text{kg}^{-1}\,\text{K}^{-1}}$$
$$= 12.1\,\text{K}$$

(to three significant figures)

(b) Energy would also be transferred to the containing tube, the temperature measuring device and the wider surroundings.

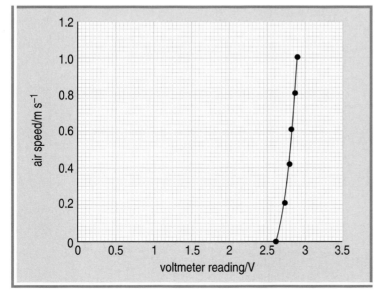

Figure 3.22
Answer to Question 10

Q13

(a) See Figure 3.23.

(b) Around 10 litres per minute.

(c) The change in temperature of the air decreases as its flow rate increases. This change in temperature, however, is clearly not inversely proportional to the flow rate as the graph is not a straight line.

Q14

$$P = \rho g h$$

$$= 1.36 \times 10^4 \, \text{kg} \, \text{m}^{-3} \times 9.81 \, \text{m} \, \text{s}^{-2} \times 0.76 \, \text{m}$$

$$= 1.014 \times 10^5 \, \text{kg} \, \text{m}^{-1} \, \text{s}^{-2}$$

$$= 1.01 \times 10^5 \, \text{N} \, \text{m}^{-2} \, \text{(or Pa)}$$

(to three significant figures)

Q15

Pressure difference $= \rho g h$

$$= 784 \, \text{kg} \, \text{m}^{-3} \times 9.81 \, \text{N} \, \text{kg}^{-1}$$

$$\times \left(15 \times 10^{-2}\right) \text{m}$$

$$= 1.2 \times 10^3 \, \text{N} \, \text{m}^{-2} \, \text{(or Pa)}$$

(to two significant figures)

Q16

As mercury is so dense, the difference between the levels in each arm of the manometer would be very small. This would make the uncertainty or error in the result very high.

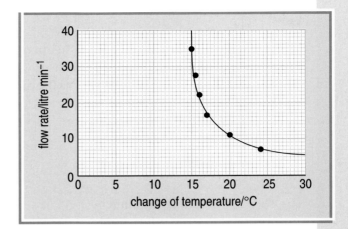

Figure 3.23 Answer to Question 13

Q17

You should have found the difference in levels to be about twice as great. Referring to Figure 3.24 you will note that, if the measured difference in levels along the tubes was L, then the vertical difference would be given by

$$h = L \sin 30°$$

$$\sin 30° = \frac{h}{L}$$

Therefore

$$h = L \times 0.5$$

since

$$\sin 30° = 0.5$$

giving you the same result as when the manometer was vertical.

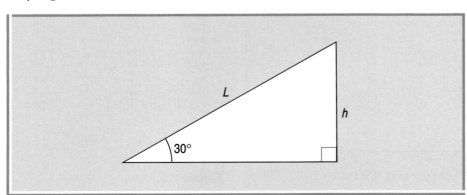

Figure 3.24
Answer to
Question 17

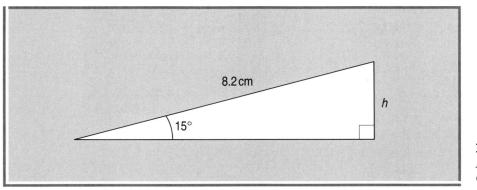

Figure 3.25
Answer to
Question 19

Q18

For low pressure differences manometers are commonly tilted at known angles.

Q19

See Figure 3.25.

$$h = L\sin 15.0°$$

$$= \left(8.20 \times 10^{-2}\right) m \times \sin 15.0°$$

$$= 2.12 \times 10^{-2} \, m$$

Therefore the pressure difference is

$$\rho g h = 784 \, kg \, m^{-3} \times 9.81 \, N \, kg^{-1} \times 2.12 \times 10^{-2} \, m$$

$$= 163 \, N \, m^{-2} \text{ or Pa}$$

    (to three significant figures)

Q20

(a) The pressure drop ΔP is given by rearranging the transfer efficiency equation

$$\text{transfer efficiency} = \frac{\Delta P}{U}$$

to give

$$\Delta P = U \times \text{transfer efficiency}$$

$$= 3.50 \times 10^{10} \, J \, m^{-3} \times 5.00 \times 10^{-4} \, Pa \, J^{-1} m^3$$

$$= 1.75 \times 10^7 \, Pa$$

(b) From this value for the pressure drop and the knowledge that the oil leaves the pipe at atmospheric pressure we can calculate the pressure required at the start of the pipe from

$$\Delta P = P_{\text{initial}} - P_{\text{final}}$$

$$P_{\text{initial}} = \Delta P + P_{\text{final}}$$

$$= 1.75 \times 10^7 \, Pa + 1 \times 10^5 \, Pa$$

$$= 1.76 \times 10^7 \, Pa$$

which is 176 atmospheres.

(c) The total pressure drop for the whole pipeline is 1.75×10^7 Pa and this will be divided equally among the pumps along its length.

$$\text{Number of pumps} = \frac{500 \, km}{10 \, km}$$

$$= 50$$

The pressure drop across each section of pipe is therefore

$$\frac{1.75 \times 10^7 \, Pa}{50} = 3.5 \times 10^5 \, Pa$$

(which is 3.5 atmospheres).

The oil must leave each pump and enter each 10 km section of pipe at

$$3.5 \times 10^5 \, Pa + 1 \times 10^5 \, Pa = 4.5 \times 10^5 \, Pa$$

(which is 4.5 atmospheres).

(d) If just one pump is used, the material and connections within the pipe would need to withstand pressures of 1.76×10^7 Pa (176 atmospheres). With pumps every 10 km the pipes need to withstand just 4.5×10^5 Pa (4.5 atmospheres). There are at least three factors that favour the lower pressures associated with the many-pump approach. Cost is perhaps the main one. A pipe produced to withstand low pressures is much less expensive than one that must withstand very high pressures. Also, if there was a leak near the start of the high-pressure pipeline much more oil would be lost compared with the same leak in a low-pressure pipeline. Safety is another crucial factor: it is much safer working on a pipe at 4.5 atmospheres than on one at 176 atmospheres.

Q21

(a) Rearranging Equation (3.2) gives

$$\frac{\Delta E}{V} = \Delta P$$

$$= 120\,\text{kPa} - 105\,\text{kPa}$$

$$= 15\,\text{kPa}$$

therefore the energy required to deliver each cubic metre of methane is 15 kJ.

Equation (3.3) also needs to be rearranged to

$$\frac{\Delta E}{V_f} = P_f \ln\left(\frac{P_i}{P_f}\right)$$

$$= 105\,\text{kPa} \times \ln\left(\frac{120\,\text{kPa}}{105\,\text{kPa}}\right)$$

$$= 105\,\text{kPa} \times 0.136$$

$$= 14\,\text{kJ}\,\text{m}^{-3}$$

Equation (3.3) is a more accurate formula and shows that energy transfer is better than predicted by Equation (3.2); but remember, the smaller ΔP is in comparison to P, the

closer these values will be. You can check this by repeating with $P_f = 115$ kPa.

(b) You need to decide which of the previous results to take. As we have the more accurate result from using Equation (3.3) we will use that.

transfer efficiency

$$= \frac{\text{energy needed to transfer the fluid}}{\text{energy that is stored in the fluid}}$$

$$= \frac{14 \times 10^3\ \text{J}\,\text{m}^{-3}}{2 \times 10^7\ \text{J}\,\text{m}^{-3}}$$

$$= 7 \times 10^{-4}$$

If you decided to use the result from Equation (3.2) you would have the following.

$$\text{transfer efficiency} = \frac{15 \times 10^3\ \text{J}\,\text{m}^{-3}}{2 \times 10^7\ \text{J}\,\text{m}^{-3}}$$

$$= 8 \times 10^{-4}$$

(to one significant figure)

Q22

$$v_1 = C\varepsilon \sqrt{\frac{2\rho_{\text{water}}\,g\Delta b}{\rho_{\text{benzene}}\left(\dfrac{A_1^2}{A_2^2} - 1\right)}}$$

$$= 1 \times 1 \sqrt{\frac{2 \times 1000\,\text{kg}\,\text{m}^{-3} \times 9.8\,\text{ms}^{-2} \times 2.0 \times 10^{-2}\,\text{m}}{879\,\text{kg}\,\text{m}^{-3} \times \left(\dfrac{\left[\pi \times \left(\dfrac{1 \times 10^{-2}\,\text{m}}{2}\right)^2\right]^2}{\left[\pi \times \left(\dfrac{0.5 \times 10^{-2}\,\text{m}}{2}\right)^2\right]^2} - 1\right)}}$$

$$= \sqrt{\frac{3.92 \times 10^2\ \text{kg}\,\text{m}^{-1}\text{s}^{-2}}{879\,\text{kg}\,\text{m}^{-3} \times (16 - 1)}}$$

$$= \sqrt{0.297\,\text{m}^2\,\text{s}^{-2}}$$

$$= 0.17\,\text{ms}^{-1}$$

Q23

(a) Substituting into the equation

$$v_1 = C\varepsilon \sqrt{\dfrac{2\rho_{mercury}\,g\Delta b}{\rho_{petrol}\left(\dfrac{A_1^2}{A_2^2}-1\right)}}$$

we have

$$v_1 = 0.98 \times 1$$

$$\times \sqrt{\dfrac{2\times13\,800\,\mathrm{kg\,m^{-3}}\times9.8\,\mathrm{m\,s^{-2}}\times78.5\times10^{-3}\,\mathrm{m}}{780\,\mathrm{kg\,m^{-3}}\times\left(\dfrac{\left[\pi\times\left(\dfrac{0.15\,\mathrm{m}}{2}\right)^2\right]^2}{\left[\pi\times\left(\dfrac{0.075\,\mathrm{m}}{2}\right)^2\right]^2}-1\right)}}$$

$$= 0.98 \times \sqrt{\dfrac{2.00\times10^4\,\mathrm{kg\,m^{-1}s^{-2}}}{780\,\mathrm{kg\,m^{-3}}\times(16-1)}}$$

$$= 0.98 \times \sqrt{1.71\,\mathrm{m^2\,s^{-2}}}$$

$$= 1.3\,\mathrm{m\,s^{-1}} \text{ (to two significant figures)}$$

(b)
Speed of flow of petrol

$$= \dfrac{\text{flow rate}}{\text{cross-sectional area of } A_1}$$

Therefore

$$\text{flow rate} = 1.3\,\mathrm{m\,s^{-1}} \times \pi \times \left(\dfrac{0.15}{2}\,\mathrm{m}\right)^2$$

$$= 0.31\,\mathrm{m^3\,s^{-1}}$$

$$\text{(to two significant figures)}$$

Q24

(a) It will be reduced to a low pressure.

(b) Some air will now get pushed in from outside to mix with the gas prior to burning at the top of the Bunsen burner.

Q25

When you squeeze the bulb, air passes out through the narrow jet and produces a low-pressure area just above the delivery tube at A. The pressure at the bottom of the delivery tube B is relatively high, being at atmospheric pressure plus that due to the small depth of perfume. The perfume will now be pushed up the delivery tube to mix with the air and through the jet to produce a fine mist.

Q26

(a)

$$\rho_{water}\,g\Delta b = 998\,\mathrm{kg\,m^{-3}} \times 9.81\,\mathrm{N\,kg^{-1}}$$

$$\times 8.00\times10^{-2}\,\mathrm{m}$$

$$= 783.2\,\mathrm{N\,m^{-2}} \text{ (or Pa)}$$

$$= 783\,\mathrm{N\,m^{-2}} \text{ (or Pa)}$$

$$\text{(to three significant figures)}$$

(b)

$$v_{air} = \sqrt{\dfrac{2\rho_{water}\,g\Delta b}{\rho_{air}\left(\dfrac{A_1^2}{A_2^2}-1\right)}}$$

$$= \sqrt{\dfrac{2\times783.2\,\mathrm{N\,m^{-2}}}{1.2\,\mathrm{kg\,m^{-3}}\times\left(\dfrac{\left[\pi\left(4.85\times10^{-3}\,\mathrm{m}\right)^2\right]^2}{\left[\pi\left(2.575\times10^{-3}\,\mathrm{m}\right)^2\right]^2}-1\right)}}$$

$$= \sqrt{\dfrac{1566.4\,\mathrm{N\,m^{-2}}}{1.2\,\mathrm{kg\,m^{-3}}\times(12.59-1)}}$$

$$= 10.61\,\mathrm{m\,s^{-1}}$$

$$= 11\,\mathrm{m\,s^{-1}} \text{ (to two significant figures)}$$

(c) $v_{calibrated} = C\varepsilon v_{air}$

so

$$8.80\,\mathrm{m\,s}^{-1} = C\varepsilon \times 10.61\,\mathrm{m\,s}^{-1}$$

giving

$$C\varepsilon = \frac{8.80\,\mathrm{m\,s}^{-1}}{10.61\,\mathrm{m\,s}^{-1}}$$

$$= 0.83 \text{ (to two significant figures)}$$

This is value is not too bad – venturimeters should have values around 0.9 or better. Much depends on the smoothness of the Bernoulli tubes, particularly at the joins of the sections. It is also difficult with an instrument like the British Gas laboratory gas meter to obtain a consistent value for the manometer levels due to the pulsation. Flow meters such as the Loflow are better.

Q27

$$P_T - P_S = \frac{1}{2}\rho_{water}v^2$$

so

$$v^2 = \frac{2(P_T - P_S)}{\rho_{water}}$$

$$= \frac{2 \times 32\,800\,\mathrm{N\,m}^{-2}}{1025\,\mathrm{kg\,m}^{-3}}$$

Therefore

$$v = \sqrt{64\,\mathrm{N\,m}^{-2}\mathrm{kg}^{-1}\mathrm{m}^3}$$

$$= 8\,\mathrm{m\,s}^{-1}$$

Q28

$$P_T - P_S = \frac{1}{2}\rho_{air}v^2$$

so

$$v^2 = \frac{2(P_T - P_S)}{\rho_{air}}$$

$$= \frac{2 \times 1 \times 10^4\,\mathrm{N\,m}^{-2}}{0.5\,\mathrm{kg\,m}^{-3}}$$

Therefore

$$v = \sqrt{4 \times 10^4\ \mathrm{N\,m}^{-2}\ \mathrm{kg}^{-1}\ \mathrm{m}^3}$$

$$= 2 \times 10^2\,\mathrm{m\,s}^{-1}$$

Q29

The Mach factor takes account of the compressibility of the air and its change of density, and the fact that the shock wave forms ahead of the tube at supersonic speeds. Other factors, such as changes due to temperature, also have to be dealt with.

Q30

(a) The pressure difference is given by

$$\rho_{water}g\Delta h = 998\,\mathrm{kg\,m}^{-3} \times 9.81\,\mathrm{m\,s}^{-2}$$

$$\times 9.0 \times 10\mathrm{m}^{-3}$$

$$= 88.11\,\mathrm{N\,m}^{-2} \text{ (or Pa)}$$

$$= 88\,\mathrm{N\,m}^{-2} \text{ (or Pa)}$$

$$\text{(to two significant figures)}$$

(b) The air speed as predicted by the pitot-static tube is given by

$$v_{air} = \sqrt{\frac{2\rho_{water}\,g\Delta b}{\rho_{air}}}$$

$$= \sqrt{\frac{2 \times 88.11\,Pa}{1.2\,kg\,m^{-3}}}$$

$$= 12.12\,ms^{-1}$$

$$= 12\,ms^{-1} \text{ (to two significant figures)}$$

(c)

$$v_{calibrated} = C\varepsilon v_{air}$$

so

$$C\varepsilon = \frac{v_{calibrated}}{v_{air}}$$

$$= \frac{8.8\,ms^{-1}}{12.12\,ms^{-1}}$$

$$= 0.73 \text{ (to two significant figures)}$$

A good-quality pitot-static tube will have a correction factor of around 0.98.

4

By now you should be well aware of the importance of fluid flow in many situations, both natural, such as rainwater running into streams and rivers and then flowing to the sea, and artificial, such as air and petrol being drawn into the carburettor of a car engine. But, in spite of the pervasiveness of fluid flow, there are just two different ways that fluid can flow. The first is laminar flow: it is orderly and predictable and it takes place when the fluid speed is sufficiently low. The second is turbulent flow: it is chaotic, unpredictable and very difficult to analyse. Laminar flow is well understood and physicists have developed useful ways to model it to make precise predictions of flow rates in given situations. Unfortunately, laminar flow hardly ever occurs in real life. Most practical applications involve turbulent flow. Oil in a long-distance pipeline flows in whirls and eddies, wasting a lot of energy in heating the oil and the pipe. Water in the penstock (the conduit between the water intake and the turbine) of a hydroelectric power station tumbles down chaotically and wastefully, lowering the overall efficiency of the whole system. Although physicists can only model these situations approximately, the models are important in maximizing the transfer efficiency of real, useful applications of fluid flow.

TWO DISTINCT FORMS OF FLUID FLOW

Turbulent flow

READY TO STUDY TEST

Before you begin this section you should be able to:

- describe the behaviour of molecules in a liquid
- relate the force on an object to the rate that its momentum is changing
- describe density in terms of mass and volume
- understand the relationship between fluid speed, mass flow rate and volume flow rate
- describe pressure in terms of force and area
- understand the behaviour of pressure in liquids
- calculate the pressure due to a column of liquid
- calculate the angular velocity of a rotating object given the number of revolutions per minute
- find the moment of a force about a given point
- find the natural logarithm ln of a number and use the inverse of this function e^x.

QUESTIONS

R1 Water is dripping from the end of a pipe. Each drop has a mass of 0.02 g and is travelling at 6 m s^{-1} when it hits the ground. calculate the average force from these drops on the ground.

R2 Ethanol has a density of 789 kg m^{-3}. Calculate the mass of 4.2 litres of ethanol.

R3 Water flows along a cylindrical pipe of radius 10.0 cm at a speed of 25.0 cm s^{-1}. Calculate the volume and mass flow rates for the water in the pipe. The density of water is $1.00 \times 10^3 \text{ kg m}^{-3}$.

R4 The water behind a dam has a depth of 30 m. If the density of water is 1000 kg m^{-3}, and using $g = 10 \text{ N kg}^{-1}$, calculate the maximum pressure difference across the dam due to the water.

R5 The pressure of gas in a particular corked bottle of champagne is 1.5 atmospheres. If the cork has a diameter of 18 mm and atmospheric pressure is 100 kPa, calculate the force that the trapped gas exerts on the cork.

R6 (a) What is the value of $\ln 5.4$? (b) What is the value of $e^{1.686399}$?

4.1 Laminar flow

When a fluid is moving slowly enough, its flow is orderly and predictable. This is called **laminar flow** and it is usually represented by **streamlines** (see Figure 4.1). Each streamline shows the path followed by packets of the fluid that are on that streamline. If you know which streamline a particular packet is on, you can predict its path through the rest of the fluid with confidence.

Streamlines in a glacier slowly moving away from Mount Everest

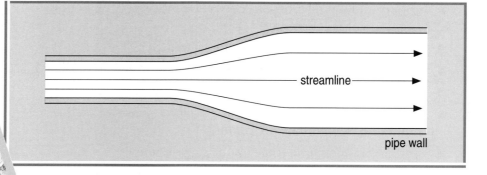

Figure 4.1 Streamlines in laminar flows

Before we look in depth at the two forms of fluid flow (laminar flow and **turbulent flow**) try the following investigation using a candle flame – it illustrates them both very clearly.

E Exploration 4.1 Investigating gas flow in a candle flame

10 MINUTES

Apparatus:

◆ candle ◆ matches ◆ clamp, boss and stand
◆ overhead projector or slide projector and screen

Place the candle between the projector and the screen as shown in Figure 4.2(a). Switch on the projector and light the candle. Shield the candle from drafts by closing doors and windows.

Look at the screen. You will see a shadow caused by the flame gas as it rises from the wick (as shown in Figure 4.2b). The shadow is caused by density variations in the hot gases; these refract the light from the projector by varying amounts as the gas passes through. Figure 4.2(b) shows that near the wick the flow of the gas is orderly. The shadows are steady, indicating that the gas flow is predictable (this is laminar flow). Further up, the flow becomes unstable. The hot gas is moving faster here – it is being accelerated upwards by the denser cold air around it. Eddies and vortices form within the gas and the whole motion becomes unpredictable and chaotic (this is turbulent flow).

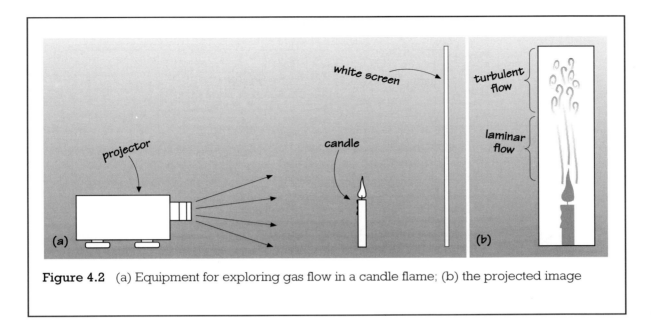

Figure 4.2 (a) Equipment for exploring gas flow in a candle flame; (b) the projected image

Velocity distribution

When we examine the speed of the fluid moving in each streamline we find that there is variation from one streamline to the next. This is due to friction.

The friction involved with laminar flow is actually relatively small. However, there is always friction because the moving fluid interacts with the stationary walls of its channel or tube. Consider water moving down the open channel in Figure 4.3. The speed of the water will depend on how far it is from the base and sides of the channel. The vectors in Figure 4.4 overleaf show a typical **velocity distribution**. Water touching the edge of the channel doesn't move at all. Water at the centre and top of the channel moves fastest. You can easily check this out by dropping sticks from a bridge over a river or stream.

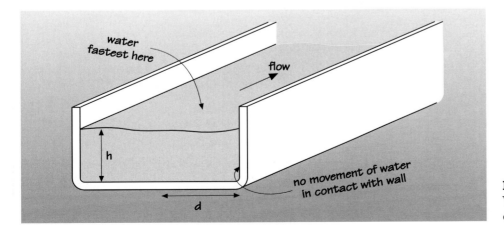

Figure 4.3
Water moving in an open channel

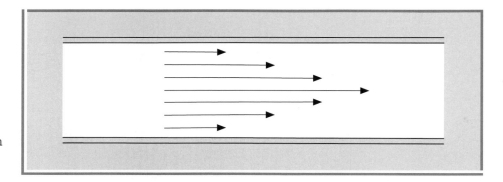

Figure 4.4
Velocity distribution
of streamlines in a
channel

Q1 Sketch a graph to show how the speed of water in laminar flow
down a cylindrical pipe depends on its distance from the walls. ◆

You have just sketched something that we call the **velocity gradient**.
This is the rate of change of velocity of the fluid with distance moved at
right angles to the streamlines.

Q2 A pair of streamlines are 1.00 cm apart. The speed of the fluid in one
is 50 mm s^{-1}, and in the other it is 20 mm s^{-1}. Calculate the velocity

gradient, $\dfrac{\Delta v}{\Delta x}$, in the fluid around these streamlines. ◆

The fact that each streamline moves at a different speed from
neighbouring streamlines means that there is also going to be friction
within the fluid itself. Look at Figure 4.5. The length of each streamline
vector indicates how fast the fluid is moving along it. As the faster layer of
fluid moves past the slower layer, a force acts on it against its motion, as
shown by the vector arrow in the opposite direction. The strength of this
force is dictated by the **viscosity** of the fluid. As the viscosity increases,
so does the frictional force between adjacent layers in the fluid. Treacle
has a higher viscosity than water, so the strength of the force acting
against relative motion between adjacent layers in the fluid is greater in
treacle than in water.

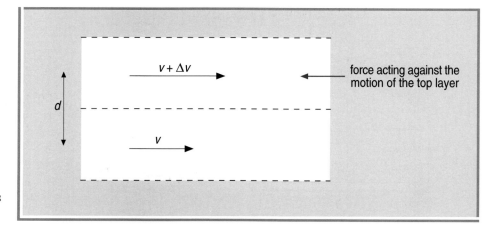

Figure 4.5
Forces acting in two
adjacent streamlines

Molecular exchange

So far we have considered streamlines without referring to the molecules within the fluid. Molecules do not stay in one streamline: they drift between layers in the fluid.

As they do this they also transfer momentum and therefore exert forces.

 What is the connection between force and momentum?

Remember Newton's second law of motion: force equals the rate of change of momentum.

Viscosity

Consider a fluid in laminar flow. The layer of fluid one side of a streamline moves faster than the layer next to it. The faster layer is slowed down by a frictional force F. Isaac Newton is said to have suggested that F depends on the area of contact of the two layers and the velocity gradient in the fluid, according to the following formula:

$$F = \eta A \frac{\Delta v}{\Delta x} \tag{4.1}$$

where F is the friction between adjacent streamlines (N), η is the viscosity of the fluid (Pa s), A is the area of contact of the streamlines (m^2) and $\frac{\Delta v}{\Delta x}$ is the velocity gradient (s^{-1}).

Q3 Show that the units of viscosity are Pa s or N s m^{-2}. ◆

Q4 A flat metal sheet lies on a flat surface. There is a film of oil 0.15 mm thick between the sheet and the surface. If the area of contact of the sheet with the surface is 0.25 m^2 and it moves at a speed of 1.0 mm per second, calculate the frictional force between the sheet and the surface. Assume that the viscosity of the oil is 50 Pa s, and that it is in laminar flow. ◆

4.2 Laminar flow through pipes

Many fluids in industry, medicine and biology are moved from one place to another along pipes and tubes. If its flow is laminar, knowing the fluid's viscosity allows us to predict accurately its flow rate down a pipe. Unfortunately, in most real situations the flow is turbulent. This means that exact prediction of flow rates is often impossible. So flow meters for real fluids have to be calibrated by making the fluid flow through at a number of different measured flow rates.

The flow rate formula

Table 4.1 lists the viscosities of some common fluids at 20°C and atmospheric pressure.

Table 4.1 Viscosity of fluids at 20°C and normal atmospheric pressure

Fluid	Viscosity/10^{-3} Pa s
Hydrogen	0.009
Air	0.018
Petrol	0.55
Water	1.00
Ethanol	1.20
Olive oil	100.00
Glycerol	1500.00

 Does a fluid with a large viscosity flow more easily than one with a small viscosity?

No. Compare water with olive oil in Table 4.1. The rate at which a fluid can flow down a pipe must depend on its viscosity. After all, by looking at Newton's formula (Equation 4.1) we can see that a high viscosity means a large amount of friction between layers of fluid that pass over each other.

What other factors might affect the flow rate?

The pressure of the fluid entering and leaving the pipe, the shape and size of its cross-section, and its length.

Over the next few paragraphs we will use the knowledge that we already have to put together a very widely used relationship for **volume flow rate**, which requires values that can be easily measured.

Figure 4.6 shows a pipe of cross-sectional area A through which a fluid is flowing with a speed v. A small volume ΔV of this fluid is shaded. It has cross-sectional area A and length Δl, so that

$$\Delta V = A\Delta l$$

We will replace A with πr^2 to give

$$\Delta V = \pi r^2 \Delta l \qquad (4.2)$$

Now

$$v = \frac{\Delta l}{\Delta t}$$

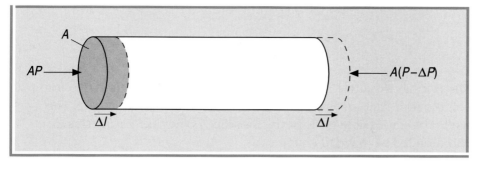

Figure 4.6
Fluid flowing through a pipe

where Δt is the time it takes our volume of fluid to move the distance Δl. If we divide both sides of Equation (4.2) by Δt we get

$$\frac{\Delta V}{\Delta t} = \pi r^2 \frac{\Delta l}{\Delta t}$$

and by replacing $\dfrac{\Delta l}{\Delta t}$ with v we get

$$\frac{\Delta V}{\Delta t} = \pi r^2 v \qquad (4.3)$$

For the next stage we need to take a different approach. Figure 4.7 is a **free body diagram** of our volume of fluid and from it we can write

$$F_1 - F_2 - R = 0$$

Where F_1 is the force due to the pressure acting on the left, F_2 is the force due to the pressure on the right and R is the resistance due to the friction between the fluid and the wall of the pipe. (We need to remember Newton's first law of motion to do this.)

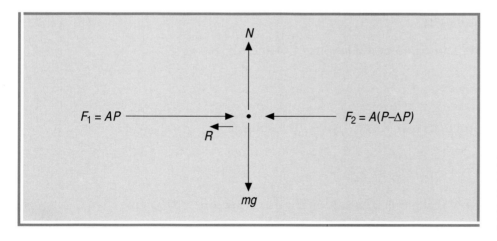

Figure 4.7
Free body diagram for a volume of fluid flowing in a horizontal pipe

If we call f the **friction per unit length** then

$$R = f \Delta l$$

and we can now write

$$AP - A(P - \Delta P) - f \Delta l = 0$$

$$A \Delta P - f \Delta l = 0$$

so

$$f = A\frac{\Delta P}{\Delta l}$$ (4.4)

The last stage that we need to go through to get our relationship for volume flow rate involves combining Equations (4.3) and (4.4). This would be impossible to do at the moment as they have no terms in common, so we have to change this.

The best way to do this is to think of how the frictional force depends on the speed of the fluid, so that we find a relationship between f and v.

 What do you think would happen to the frictional force per unit length f if the velocity v is doubled?

If v is doubled, f would also double.

Now we can write

$$f \propto v$$

and so

$$f = Cv$$ (4.5)

Where C is the constant of proportionality.

 What will be the units of C?

The same as those for viscosity: Pa s or N s m^{-2}.

This relationship gives us the link that we need between Equations (4.3) and (4.4).

We can combine Equations (4.4) and (4.5) to give

$$Cv = A\frac{\Delta P}{\Delta l}$$

and rearrange this to make v the subject

$$v = \frac{A}{C}\frac{\Delta P}{\Delta l}$$

Now make this substitution for v in Equation (4.3) to give

$$\frac{\Delta V}{\Delta t} = \pi r^2 \frac{A}{C}\frac{\Delta P}{\Delta l}$$

and so

$$\frac{\Delta V}{\Delta t} = \frac{\left(\pi r^2\right)^2}{C}\frac{\Delta P}{\Delta l}$$ (4.6)

Looking at Equation (4.6) we can see that for a particular pipe the volume flow rate will depend only on the pressure gradient (all the other values on the right-hand side being constants). If we change to a pipe with twice the radius, Equation (4.6) shows that the volume flow rate will increase sixteen-fold!

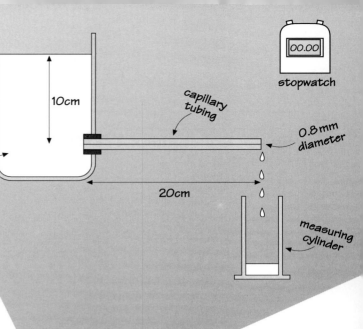

Detailed analysis shows that the constant $C = 8\pi\eta$. Jean Poiseuille (1797–1869) first discovered this and so we call the final version of this relationship Poiseuille's formula:

$$\frac{\Delta V}{\Delta t} = \frac{\pi r^4}{8\eta}\frac{\Delta P}{\Delta l} \qquad (4.7)$$

 What happens to the volume flow rate if the same system is used to transfer a fluid with twice the viscosity?

The volume flow rate would halve.

Figure 4.8
Apparatus to measure the viscosity of water

Poiseuille's formula shows why a slight narrowing of arteries leading to heart muscles can have such drastic consequences. A certain minimum flow of blood through these arteries is needed to keep the heart muscle supplied with enough oxygen and nutrients to keep it operating. Poor diet and lack of exercise can result in layers of fatty material being deposited on the walls of arteries. If the radius drops by just 16% the flow rate is halved. The consequences can be lethal.

 What does a 10% drop in radius do to the flow rate if the pressure gradient is unchanged?

If the radius becomes 90% of its previous value, r^4 in Poiseuille's formula (Equation 4.7) becomes $(0.9r)^4 = 0.66r^4$. So the flow rate drops to 66% of its previous value.

Q5 What happens to the volume flow rate down a tube if all of its dimensions are doubled? ◆

Q6 The apparatus shown in Figure 4.8 can be used to measure the viscosity of water. The length of the capillary tube is 20 cm and its diameter is 0.80 mm. If the surface of the water is 10 cm above the tube, calculate the pressure gradient and volume flow rates in the tube. The density and viscosity of water are 1000 kg m^{-3} and 0.001 Pa s, respectively. ◆

Exploration 4.2 will allow you to verify Poiseuille's formula for water and other liquids.

E **Exploration 4.2   Exploring laminar flow**

50 MINUTES

Apparatus:

◆ stand, ring clamp, clamps and bosses ◆ large plastic fizzy lemonade bottle with the base cut off ◆ bung fitted with glass tube ◆ 100 cm thin-wall rubber tubing
◆ 15 cm (or longer) of 1 mm diameter (or less) glass capillary tube ◆ metre rule
◆ stopwatch ◆ 10 ml measuring cylinder ◆ large plastic beaker ◆ petroleum jelly

Arrange the apparatus as shown in Figure 4.9, making sure the capillary tube is horizontal. The rubber tubing must be securely fixed to the glass tube in the bung, and the bung must be firmly jammed in the neck of the bottle. Fill the bottle with cold water from the tap. A dab of petroleum jelly on the open end of the capillary tube helps the water to drop off at low flow rates.

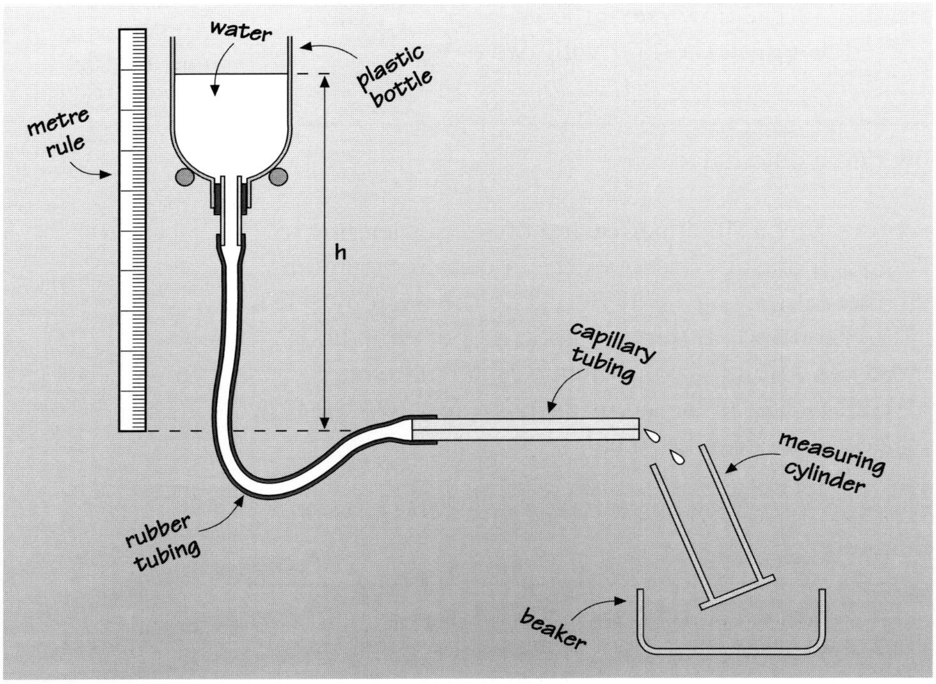

Figure 4.9 Equipment for exploring laminar flow

For various values of h (the distance from the surface of the water to the capillary tube), measure the time t for exactly 10 cm^3 of water to flow out of the end of the capillary tube.

For each value of h, use the formula $P = \rho g h$ to calculate the pressure drop that is forcing water through the capillary tube. Assume that $\rho = 1000$ kg m^{-3}. Hence calculate the pressure gradient $\dfrac{\Delta P}{\Delta l}$. Similarly, for each value of t, calculate the volume flow rate $\dfrac{\Delta V}{\Delta t}$. Then plot a graph of volume flow rate as a function of pressure gradient as in

Figure 4.10. If you obtain a straight line, measure the gradient and use it to determine a value for the viscosity of water.

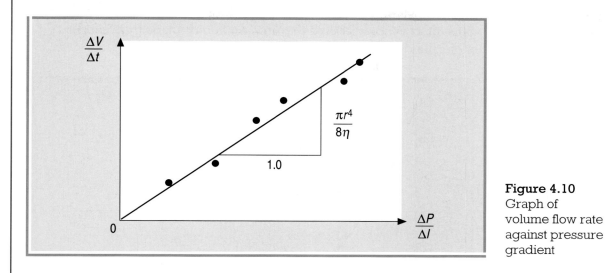

Figure 4.10
Graph of volume flow rate against pressure gradient

You could repeat the experiment for different capillary tubes. The length must be at least 15 cm and the diameter less than 1 mm for the flow to be laminar. This will allow you to verify that the flow rate is proportional to the fourth power of the radius.

JEAN POISEUILLE (1797–1869)

Jean Poiseuille was a doctor working in Paris when he discovered the important parts of the formula that now bears his name. His main interest was studying the way that blood flows around the human body. He invented the use of a mercury manometer to measure blood pressure. This replaced the crude method invented by Hales which involved long vertical glass tubes inserted directly into veins and arteries. In order to find out more about the circulation of the blood, Poiseuille investigated the flow of distilled water down lengths of capillary tube with diameters ranging from 0.03 mm to 0.14 mm. Previous researchers had used tubes with much larger diameters and had failed to discover any clear relationships because of turbulence. Poiseuille was also lucky in another way. He published his results in 1840, one year after G. H. L. Hagen. It took several years for the physics community to realize this, by which time Poiseuille's name was irretrievably glued to his formula. Incidentally, Poiseuille didn't even make the link with viscosity. However, once he had published his discovery, physicists were soon able to show mathematically that $C = 8\pi\eta$.

Hot fluids flow faster

The graph in Figure 4.11 shows how the viscosity of water varies with temperature. As you can see, the viscosity starts off dropping rapidly with increasing temperature and that the rate of change gradually reduces. This effect is not restricted to water. All liquids made from simple molecules behave in this way.

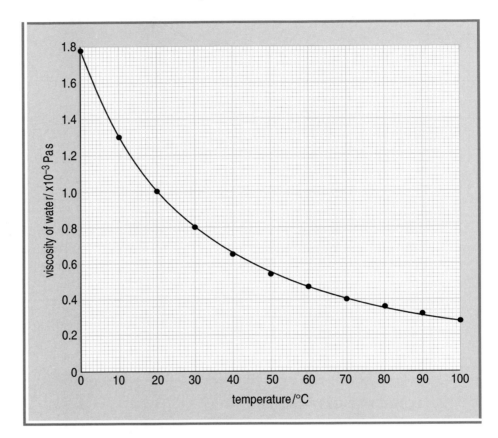

Figure 4.11
Graph of viscosity of water against temperature

Engine lubrication

This change in viscosity clearly has implications for the design of internal combustion engines and for the choice of lubricants, since these engines start off cold but run hot.

Lubrication is needed to reduce the effects of friction, especially the thermal energy that friction generates (the amount of thermal energy generated by friction is quite clear to anyone who has warmed their hands by rubbing them together). Without a protective low-friction layer, friction would quickly melt the two parts of a bearing into each other. The bearing and possibly the whole engine would be destroyed.

In normal running, the oil that runs out of the bearings and into the sump is filtered and pumped straight back into the bearings. Because of the change in viscosity with temperature, an oil with optimum viscosity at the running temperature will be far too viscous for lubrication when the engine starts from cold. As a result, the pump may not be able to deliver enough of the oil to the bearings when the engine is started, resulting in undue wear.

It is for this reason that modern engine oils are not just long-chain hydrocarbons. They also contain additives that prevent the viscosity from dropping too rapidly as the oil heats up. The aim is to construct a liquid whose viscosity is independent of temperature.

 Bitumen is a black liquid made from long-chain hydrocarbons. It is used for surfacing roads. Why is the bitumen used in the UK unsuitable for use in hot climates? (And even on some days in our climate!)

Its viscosity falls as temperature rises. So if it gets too hot, it will flow out from under tyres, and the road surface will become distorted.

4.3 Modelling viscosity in liquids

Solids have a fixed shape because their individual particles (molecules, ions or atoms) do not have enough energy to escape the clutches of their neighbours. A liquid can be thought of as a solid where some of the particles have gained enough energy to move elsewhere. This means that a liquid can change its shape, but only as fast as its particles can find the energy to change places with each other. That energy comes from the kinetic energy continuously exchanged at random between all of the particles in the liquid. As the temperature goes up, so does the kinetic energy, so more particles can escape from their neighbours and move to a new position.

If you have worked through the SLIPP unit *Physics on a Plate* you will have come across an equation that gives us the average kinetic energy $\langle E \rangle$ (or $\langle E_k \rangle$) of a particle in a substance at temperature T (measured in kelvin). This equation is

$$\langle E \rangle = \frac{3}{2}kT \tag{4.8}$$

where k is a constant of proportionality called the Boltzmann constant – its value is 1.38×10^{-23} J K^{-1}. It is named after Ludwig Boltzmann, an Austrian physicist.

LUDWIG BOLTZMANN (1844–1906)

Ludwig Boltzmann spent much of his working life as a professor of physics in Vienna and Munich. He was jointly responsible with James Clerk Maxwell for the kinetic theory of gases. This theory showed how Newton's laws of motion could be used to explain the behaviour of gases. Boltzmann was one of the first to grasp the full significance of the concept of energy introduced by James Joule. His ideas of things being hotter as a result of the increased random kinetic energy of their particles became the basis of statistical mechanics, a branch of physics that gives theoretical underpinning to thermodynamics. Boltzmann had a lot of trouble convincing his colleagues that his ideas were correct and grew very depressed over this. Ironically, one year after his death, Albert Einstein published a paper that used Boltzmann's ideas to explain the random motion of microscopically small particles suspended in water first noticed by the botanist Robert Brown in 1827. For most physicists, this was regarded as proof of the existence of atoms for the first time, and Boltzmann's ideas have remained at the centre of physics ever since. Boltzmann had such confidence in his work that he had his equation for entropy ($S = k \log W$) engraved on his tombstone.

Boltzmann's tomb

You will have also come across the idea that there is a large spread of molecular energies in a sample of a substance. At an instant in time some molecules will have low energies and some will have high energies. At another instant in time there will continue to be the same proportions with low and with high energies, although they will be different molecules.

Ludwig Boltzmann also discovered that he could predict the proportion of molecules, P, with a particular energy, E, using the equation

$$P = e^{-E/kT} \tag{4.9}$$

At very low temperatures, P is also very low: it drops towards zero as the temperature is reduced towards absolute zero. As the temperature of the fluid increases, P also increases towards its maximum value

 What is the maximum value of P?

As the value of T increases, the value of $\dfrac{E}{kT}$ decreases. If T could become infinitely large, $\dfrac{E}{kT}$ would reduce to zero. At this point $P = e^0$, which equals 1, as anything raised to the power zero is one.

This is how viscosity drops with increasing temperature: more molecules have sufficient energy to swap places, making it easier to change the shape of the liquid.

The relationship between viscosity and temperature T (measured in kelvin) is

$$\eta = \eta_0 e^{E/kT} \qquad (4.10)$$

where η_0 is the minimum viscosity.

This shows that viscosity drops exponentially with increasing temperature.

If we are to check this relationship we need to measure the viscosity of a liquid over a range of temperatures and plot the results. There is a snag with this approach here though: how can we be sure that it is an exponential curve? In fact, rather than come up with a way of testing this curve it is very much easier to change what we plot.

To help us decide what to plot we manipulate the equation into a form that will give a straight-line graph if it is correct. If is quite easy to judge whether points lie on a straight line or not and we can also learn from the values of the slope and the intercept. Taking natural logarithms of each side of Equation (4.10) gives

$$\ln \eta = \ln \eta_0 + \ln e^{E/kT}$$

and since $\ln e^{E/kT}$ is equal to $\dfrac{E}{kT}$

$$\ln \eta = \ln \eta_0 + \dfrac{E}{kT}$$

or

$$\ln \eta = \dfrac{E}{kT} + \ln \eta_0$$

which is in the form of an equation of a straight line: $y = mx + c$.

If we plot the natural logarithm of our measurements of viscosity against $\dfrac{1}{kT}$, the slope should be E and the intercept will be $\ln \eta_0$.

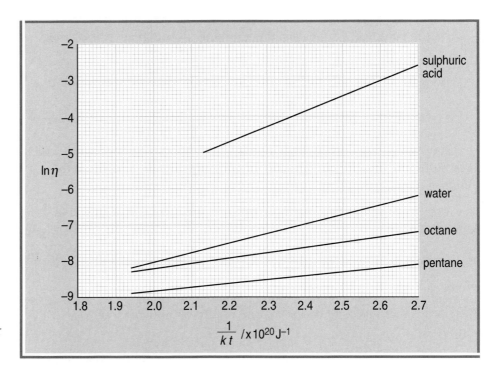

Figure 4.12
The relationship between viscosity and temperature for several liquids

Figure 4.12 shows the curves plotted for several real liquids. The curves do closely fit straight lines and therefore the viscosities of the liquids drop exponentially with increasing temperature.

Q7 The viscosity of castor oil is 2.4 Pa s at 10°C and 1.0 Pa s at 20°C. Take the value for k as 1.38×10^{-23} J K^{-1}.

(a) Find the value of E.

(b) Find the value of η_0.

(c) Use these two values to predict the viscosity at 100°C (373 K). ◆

Exploration 4.3 will allow you to verify the Boltzmann model of the variation of water's viscosity with temperature. You can even obtain a value for the energy needed to move one molecule of water away from its neighbours!

Apparatus:

◆ 5 cm length of 0.5 mm diameter (or less) capillary tubing ◆ 7 cm length of 5 mm diameter glass tubing ◆ short plastic rule marked in cm ◆ thermometer ◆ 5 mm rubber tubing ◆ rubber bands ◆ large glass beaker ◆ stopwatch ◆ kettle ◆ ice ◆ dropper

Use Figure 4.13 to help you to set up the equipment. Once everything is in place, pour tap water into the beaker to a depth of 25 mm. Fill up the tube to the top with a dropper, making sure that there are no air bubbles in the tube.

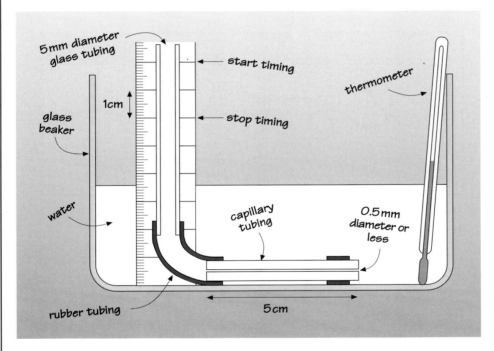

Figure 4.13
Experimental set-up for Exploration 4.3

Let the water in the tube drain into the beaker through the capillary tube. Record the time t it takes for the water to drop between the 8 cm and 6 cm marks on the rule (see Figure 4.13). Note the temperature of the water T in kelvin. Repeat several times using water at a number of different temperatures between 0°C and 100°C. You will have to let the system settle down to its new temperature before taking measurements. Make sure that your water is clean; it is easy to block the capillary tube.

If the flow through the capillary tube is laminar, the flow rate should be proportional to the viscosity η. The volume flow rate is proportional to $\Delta l/\Delta t$ where Δl is the distance that the water has dropped (2 cm). So plot a graph of $\ln(\Delta l/\Delta t)$ against $1/kT$. If you can fit a straight line through the points, the Boltzmann model of viscosity has been verified. The gradient of the graph should give you a value for E, the energy needed to move one molecule of water away from its neighbours.

4.4 Turbulent flow in pipes

You should now have some clear ideas about the predictable laminar flow that we sometimes see, but there are many occasions when these are not enough. So we will now turn our attention to turbulent flow.

Fast-flowing fluids become unstable. Instead of the orderly motion that we have considered so far, with each parcel of the fluid following a streamline, the motion becomes chaotic and unpredictable; it loops and whirls around, apparently at random, as in Figure 4.14. Turbulent flow down a pipe is wasteful compared with laminar flow. You need a larger pressure gradient to force the fluid through, leading to a greater expenditure of energy.

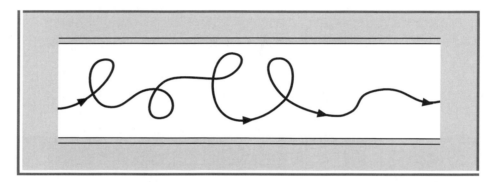

Figure 4.14
The motion of a parcel of fluid

Reynolds number

When a fluid flows down a pipe with a circular cross-section, if its average speed is below a certain value, known as the **critical velocity**, v_c, the flow is laminar. If its average speed is above this value, the flow becomes turbulent.

Osborne Reynolds, a British engineer, discovered a relationship between the inertial and the viscous forces in a fluid. He found empirically (by experiment) that the ratio of these forces was a constant. This dimensionless constant became known as the Reynolds number, R, which is defined by equation

$$R = \frac{\text{inertial forces}}{\text{viscous forces}}$$

(*Note:* Dimensionless just means that there are no units associated with the number.)

It turns out that ρv_c^2 is proportional to the inertia of the fluid and $\eta \dfrac{v_c}{r}$ is proportional to the viscous forces, where ρ is the density of the fluid

(kg s m^{-3}); v_{c} is the critical velocity (m s^{-1}), η is the viscosity (Pa s) and r is the pipe's radius (m). So

$$R = \frac{\rho v_{c}^{2}}{\eta \dfrac{v_{c}}{r}}$$

$$= \frac{\rho v_{c} r}{\eta}$$

So, for a pipe with a circular cross-section, the critical velocity is given by:

$$v_{c} = R\frac{\eta}{\rho r}$$

The apparatus used is shown in Figure 4.15. Water flows down a long glass tube from left to right. Some ink is injected into the centre of the water. As the flow rate down the tube is increased, the ink ceases to move down the centre of the tube and starts to move in random whirls and eddies. At high enough flow rates, the ink is completely mixed up with the water. The value of the Reynolds number depends on the exact geometry of the pipe, how rough the surfaces are and how evident the turbulence has to be. For a perfectly smooth pipe of circular cross-section, a value of R of about 1000 would give totally chaotic flow. However, in the real world, R values as low as 20 may be associated with turbulent flow – it just depends on the nature of the pipe.

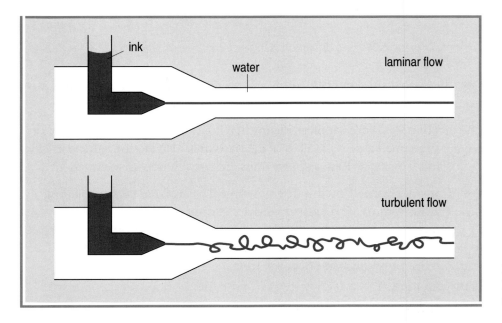

Figure 4.15
Reynolds'
apparatus

OSBORNE REYNOLDS (1842–1912)

Reynolds worked in many areas of physics during his 37 years as Professor of Engineering in Manchester. They included work on the design of pumps and turbines, radiometers, the flow of heat energy in liquids, and the precision measurement of the specific heat capacity of water. His most famous piece of work was also one of his earliest. In 1883, he published a paper on turbulence, describing the results of his experiments to determine the conditions under which laminar flow becomes turbulent. In 1886, he produced an important theory of thin film lubrication. This made possible the design of bearings that could take high loads at much higher speeds than were previously thought possible. Towards the end of his working life, Reynolds appears to have turned his thoughts to a Theory of Everything. Having been an engineer all his life, despite being a top maths student at Cambridge, he couldn't escape from his mechanical roots. Reynolds envisaged a universe made entirely from rigid granules that were free to slide past each other. At a lecture in 1902 he said 'I have in my hand the first experimental model universe, a soft india rubber bag … filled with lead shot … [I have] the fullest confidence that … ideas, such as I have endeavoured to sketch, will ultimately prevail.' Reynolds' ideas about the structure of the universe were highly regarded at that time. Now, of course, his mechanical model has been superseded and is largely forgotten. One might wonder what is the destiny of today's mathematical models?

Q8 Show that the Reynolds number has no dimensions (i.e. that it has no units associated with it). ◆

The fact that R is dimensionless means that it has the interesting property of having the same value regardless of the base units used to measure viscosity, radius and density, as long as these units are consistent with each other.

Q9 Consider water flowing down a typical microbore central heating pipe (radius 6 mm). The critical velocity is only 0.17 m s^{-1}. So if you want to deliver water at more than 20 cm^3 s^{-1} through such a pipe, it will have to be turbulent flow. Show that the following statements, which were made in the previous sentence, are true.

(a) $v_c = 0.17$ m s^{-1}.

(b) Turbulent flow is required to deliver volume flow rates above 20 cm^3 s^{-1}.

Take the density of water to be 1000 kg m^{-3} and its viscosity to be 0.001 Pa s. ◆

4.5 Turbulent flow rates

When the flow is laminar, the friction per metre of pipe is proportional to the fluid's velocity. Turbulence not only increases the amount of friction, it also results in the friction being proportional to the square of the velocity, which means we need to modify our equation for volume flow.

When the flow is laminar, the volume flow rate is given by Poiseuille's formula, which you came across earlier in this section.

$$\frac{\Delta V}{\Delta t} = \frac{\pi r^4}{8\eta} \frac{\Delta P}{\Delta l} \qquad \text{(Equation 4.7)}$$

When the flow in a pipe becomes turbulent, we have to use a different equation.

$$\frac{\Delta V}{\Delta t} = \sqrt{\left(\frac{\pi^2 R r^5}{8\rho}\right) \frac{\Delta P}{\Delta l}} \qquad (4.11)$$

Where again r is the radius of the pipe, ρ is the density of the liquid, $\frac{\Delta P}{\Delta l}$ is the pressure gradient (in Pa m^{-1}) and R is the Reynolds number.

For rough calculations we can use $R = 1000$. The value of R in any particular system will depend on just how smooth and straight the pipes are. It also is dependent on viscosity, which varies greatly with temperature.

Q10 Water is flowing turbulently down a pipe of diameter 13 mm at a rate of 1 kg s^{-1}. Do a calculation to estimate the pressure gradient required if water has a density of 1000 kg m^{-3}. Assume that $R = 1000$. ◆

Q11 Table 4.2 contains data obtained with apparatus similar to that described in Exploration 4.2. The capillary tube had a diameter of 0.9 mm and a length of 5 cm. The liquid was water (density 1000 kg m^{-3}, viscosity 0.001 Pa s) and $g = 9.81$ m s^{-2}. As in Exploration 4.2, h is the distance from the surface of the water to the capillary tube and t is the time taken to collect 10 cm^3 of liquid.

Table 4.2

h/m	t/s
0.890	6.46
0.735	6.95
0.575	7.10
0.490	7.85
0.304	10.84
0.200	12.86

(a) Use the data to add columns to the table to show how the volume flow rate and pressure gradient vary.

(b) Plot a graph of volume flow rate against pressure gradient and describe how this shows that the flow is not laminar.

(c) Plot a graph of the flow rate against the square root of the pressure gradient. Draw a best straight line through the points. What does this tell you about the nature of the flow? Use the gradient of the graph to calculate the value of the Reynolds number, R. ◆

Exploration 4.4 gives you the chance to investigate the turbulent flow of water through the nozzle of a burette.

Exploration 4.4   Exploring turbulent flow

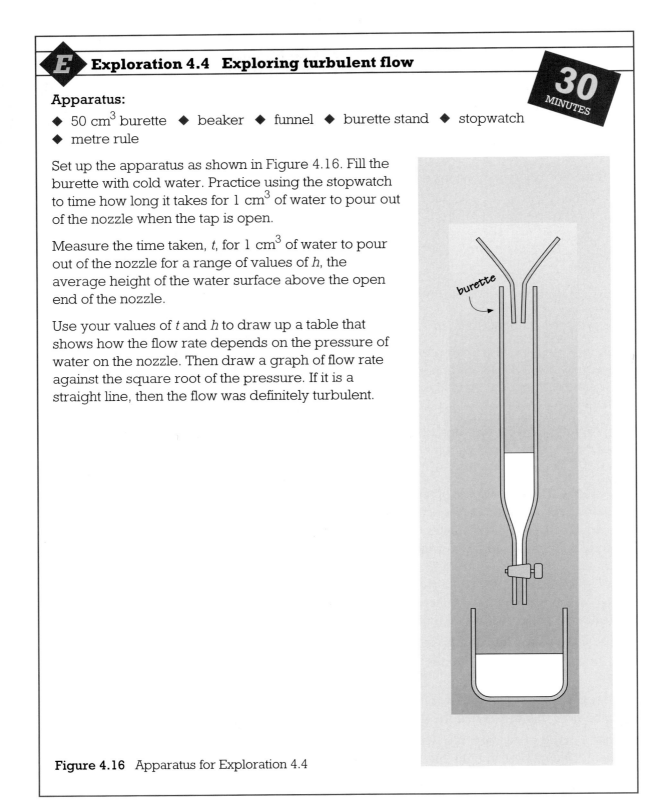

Apparatus:

- 50 cm^3 burette ◆ beaker ◆ funnel ◆ burette stand ◆ stopwatch
- metre rule

Set up the apparatus as shown in Figure 4.16. Fill the burette with cold water. Practice using the stopwatch to time how long it takes for 1 cm^3 of water to pour out of the nozzle when the tap is open.

Measure the time taken, t, for 1 cm^3 of water to pour out of the nozzle for a range of values of h, the average height of the water surface above the open end of the nozzle.

Use your values of t and h to draw up a table that shows how the flow rate depends on the pressure of water on the nozzle. Then draw a graph of flow rate against the square root of the pressure. If it is a straight line, then the flow was definitely turbulent.

30 MINUTES

burette

Figure 4.16 Apparatus for Exploration 4.4

4.6 Transporting energy

Figure 4.17 shows how the pressure gradient along a pipe varies with the volume flow rate through it. Low pressure gradients result in laminar flow, with the flow rate proportional to the pressure gradient. High pressure gradients result in turbulent flow, with the flow rate proportional to the square root of the pressure gradient. As an illustration of what this means in practice, consider an oil pipeline like the one shown on p. 50. If it takes 1 MJ of work to transport 100 MJ of energy down the pipeline at maximum velocity for laminar flow, then it takes 4 MJ to transport that 100 MJ in half the time. In other words, doubling the flow rate by using turbulent flow has required the use of four times as much energy.

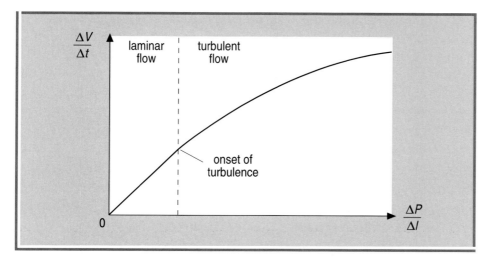

Figure 4.17
Graph of pressure gradient against volume flow rate in a pipe

> ❓ How much energy would be needed to transport 100 MJ of chemical energy at ten times the critical velocity?

100 MJ. It wouldn't be worth doing. It would be much better to build ten identical pipelines in parallel.

Q12 An oil pipeline has a length of 500 km and a radius of 40 cm. The oil has a density of 860 kg m^{-3} and a viscosity of 5.0×10^{-3} Pa s and is pumped with a pressure gradient of 30 kPa per kilometre.

(a) Estimate the flow rate of the oil, assuming that $R = 1000$, i.e. turbulent flow.

(b) Calculate the average velocity of the oil. Hence show that the flow is definitely turbulent.

(c) The energy density of oil is 3.5×10^{10} J m^{-3}. Calculate the transfer efficiency for the pipeline.

(d) What happens to the transfer efficiency if the flow rate is doubled by increasing the pressure gradient? ◆

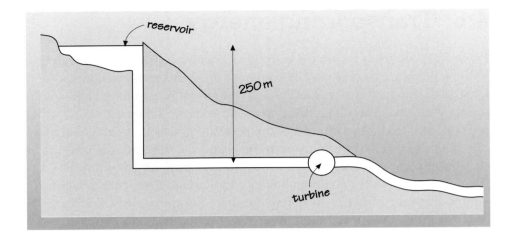

Figure 4.18
A hydroelectric
power station

Q13 Figure 4.18 shows the basic arrangements of a typical hydroelectric
power station. Water drops a vertical height of 250 m through a pipe of
diameter 3.25 m and length 1.2 km. It accelerates through a nozzle and
electricity is generated in a turbine. Each cubic metre passing through the
nozzle results in 1.2 MJ of electricity. The density and viscosity of water
are 1000 kg m^{-3} and 0.001 Pa s, respectively.

(a) If the flow of water in the pipe is laminar, what is the maximum
volume flow rate?

(b) What is the maximum power output of the system if the flow down
the pipe is laminar?

(c) How much energy is required to push a cubic metre of water down
the pipe at the critical velocity?

(d) Compare your answers to (c) and (b). Is it important to keep the flow
in the pipe laminar if the turbine efficiency is only 50%? ◆

Q14 This question deals with the same hydroelectric power station as
Question 13. To obtain an output power of 50 MW from the generator,
the flow of water in the pipe has to be turbulent.

(a) Calculate the required volume flow rate of water through the pipe.

(b) Do a calculation to estimate the work done transporting 1 m^3 of water
down the pipe. Assume that $R = 1000$. Compare it to the electricity
created by that cubic metre of water. ◆

Achievements

After working through this section you should be able to:

- describe the difference between laminar and turbulent flow

- perform an experiment to demonstrate laminar and turbulent flow in air

- describe the idea of streamlines

- sketch velocity distributions for fluids in laminar flow down pipes and channels

- quote Newton's formula for the friction force between layers of fluid in laminar flow: $F = \eta A \dfrac{\Delta v}{\Delta x}$

- give a particle model to account for Newton's formula

- explain that viscosity is a measure of the friction involved in making a fluid move in laminar flow

- calculate the volume flow rate from the average velocity of a fluid

- explain that the friction per unit length is proportional to the average velocity for laminar flow

- use Poiseuille's formula: $\dfrac{\Delta V}{\Delta t} = \dfrac{\pi r^4}{8\eta}\dfrac{\Delta P}{\Delta l}$

- perform an experiment to measure the viscosity of a liquid

- understand that viscosity decreases with increasing temperature.

- use Boltzmann's formula to predict the variation of viscosity with temperature: $\eta = \eta_0 e^{E/kT}$

- perform an experiment to measure the variation of viscosity with temperature for a liquid

- calculate the critical velocity of a liquid flowing down a pipe using the formula: $v_{c} = R\dfrac{\eta}{\rho r}$

- state that the friction per unit length is proportional to the square of the average velocity for a fluid in turbulent flow

- calculate approximate flow rates for liquids in turbulent flow down circular pipes using the formula: $\dfrac{\Delta V}{\Delta t} = \sqrt{\left(\dfrac{\pi^2 R r^5}{8\rho}\right)\dfrac{\Delta P}{\Delta l}}$

- estimate transfer efficiencies for liquid fuels transported in pipes by turbulent flow.

Glossary

Critical velocity The highest value of the fluid velocity at which the flow is laminar.

Free body diagram A diagram of one part (usually a body) in a system drawn in isolation from surfaces or other bodies with which it is in contact or interaction, so that the forces acting on the body (rather than the forces from the body acting on the surfaces or other body) can be drawn.

Friction per unit length The frictional force acting on a metre length of a fluid due to its interaction with the walls of its container.

Laminar flow A fluid is in laminar flow if all portions of the fluid that pass a particular point follow the same path from then on.

Streamline The path followed by a parcel of fluid in laminar flow.

Turbulent flow   A fluid is in turbulent flow if the trajectory of a parcel of fluid is unpredictable.

Velocity distribution   A graph that shows the variation of velocity across a pipe or channel.

Velocity gradient   The rate at which the velocity of a fluid in laminar flow varies along a path at right angles to the flow direction.

Viscosity   The force per unit area between adjacent layers of fluid in laminar flow for a velocity gradient of one.

Volume flow rate   The volume of fluid that passes a point in a pipe or channel in one second.

Answers to Ready to Study test

R1

Newton's second law says that force equals the rate of change of momentum (momentum = mv)

$$F = \frac{\text{change in momentum}}{\text{change in time}}$$

$$= \frac{\Delta(mv)}{\Delta t}$$

$$= \frac{200 \times 0.02 \times 10^{-3}\,\text{kg} \times 6\,\text{ms}^{-1}}{60\,\text{s}}$$

$$= 4 \times 10^{-4}\,\text{N}$$

R2

$$\rho = \frac{m}{V}$$

so

$$m = \rho V$$

$$= 789\,\text{kg}\,\text{m}^{-3} \times 4.2 \times 10^{-3}\,\text{m}^3$$

$$= 3.3\,\text{kg} \text{ (to two significant figures)}$$

R3

$$\frac{\Delta V}{\Delta t} = \pi r^2 v$$

$$= \pi \times \left(10.0 \times 10^{-2}\,\text{m}\right)^2 \times 0.250\,\text{ms}^{-1}$$

$$= 7.85 \times 10^{-3}\,\text{m}^3\,\text{s}^{-1}$$

$$\text{(to three significant figures)}$$

$$m = \rho V$$

so

$$\frac{\Delta m}{\Delta t} = \rho \frac{\Delta V}{\Delta t}$$

$$= 1.00 \times 10^3\,\text{kg}\,\text{m}^{-3} \times 7.85 \times 10^{-3}\,\text{m}^3\,\text{s}^{-1}$$

$$= 7.85\,\text{kg}\,\text{s}^{-1}$$

R4

$$P = \rho g h$$

$$= 1000\,\text{kg}\,\text{m}^{-3} \times 10\,\text{N}\,\text{kg}^{-1} \times 30\,\text{m}$$

$$= 3 \times 10^5\,\text{Pa}$$

R5

$$P = \frac{F}{A}$$

and

$$A = \pi r^2$$

$$= \pi \times \left(9 \times 10^{-3}\,\text{m}\right)^2$$

$$= 2.54 \times 10^{-4}\,\text{m}^2$$

so

$$F = PA$$

$$= 1.5 \times 100 \times 10^3\,\text{Pa} \times 2.54 \times 10^{-4}\,\text{m}^2$$

$$= 38\,\text{N} \text{ (to two significant figures)}$$

R6

(a) 1.686 399.

(b) 5.4.

Answers to questions in the text

Q1

See Figure 4.19.

Q2

$$\frac{\Delta v}{\Delta x} = \frac{(50-20)\times 10^{-3}\,\text{ms}^{-1}}{1.00\times 10^{-2}\,\text{m}}$$

$$= 3.0\,\text{s}^{-1}$$

Q3

$$F = \eta A \frac{\Delta v}{\Delta x}$$

$$\eta = \frac{F\Delta x}{A\Delta v}$$

so the units of η are

$$\frac{\text{N m}}{\text{m}^2\,\text{m s}^{-1}}$$

which reduces to N s m^{-2} or Pa s.

Q4

$$F = \eta A \frac{\Delta v}{\Delta x}$$

$$= 50\,\text{Pa s}\times 0.25\,\text{m}^2 \times \frac{1.0\times 10^{-3}\,\text{ms}^{-1}}{0.15\times 10^{-3}\,\text{m}}$$

$$= 83\,\text{N (to two significant figures)}$$

Q5

$$\frac{\Delta V_1}{\Delta t_1} = \frac{\pi r^4}{8\eta}\frac{\Delta P}{\Delta l}$$

if r becomes $2r$ and Δl becomes $2\Delta l$ then

$$\frac{\Delta V_2}{\Delta t_2} = \frac{\pi(2r)^4}{8\eta}\frac{\Delta P}{2\Delta l}$$

$$= \frac{8\pi r^4}{8\eta}\frac{\Delta P}{\Delta l}$$

$$= 8\frac{\Delta V_1}{\Delta t_1}$$

So the volume flow rate increases eight-fold.

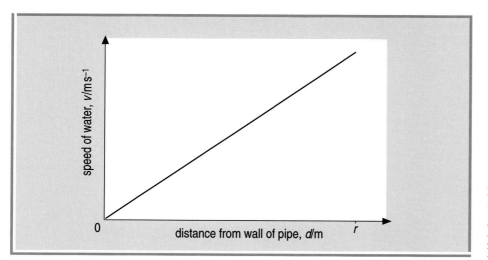

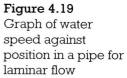

Figure 4.19
Graph of water speed against position in a pipe for laminar flow

Q6

$$P = \rho g b$$

$$= 1000\,\mathrm{kg\,m^{-3}} \times 9.8\,\mathrm{N\,kg^{-1}} \times 0.1\,\mathrm{m}$$

$$= 980\,\mathrm{Pa}$$

therefore the pressure gradient is

$$\frac{\Delta P}{\Delta l} = \frac{980\,\mathrm{Pa}}{0.20\,\mathrm{m}}$$

$$= 4.9 \times 10^3\,\mathrm{Pa\,m^{-1}}$$

and the volume flow rate is

$$\frac{\Delta V}{\Delta t} = \frac{\pi r^4}{8\eta}\frac{\Delta P}{\Delta l}$$

$$= \frac{\pi \times \left(0.40 \times 10^{-3}\,\mathrm{m}\right)^4}{8 \times 0.001\,\mathrm{Pa\,s}} \times 4.9 \times 10^3\,\mathrm{Pa\,m^{-1}}$$

$$= 4.9 \times 10^{-8}\,\mathrm{m^3\,s^{-1}}$$

(to two significant figures)

Q7

(a) $\eta = \eta_0 e^{+E/kT}$

so

$$\ln\eta = \ln\eta_0 + \frac{E}{kT}$$

At 10°C

$$\ln 2.4 = \ln\eta_0 + \frac{E}{1.38 \times 10^{-23}\,\mathrm{J\,K^{-1}} \times 283\,\mathrm{K}}$$

so

$$0.875 = \ln\eta_0 + 2.560 \times 10^{20}\,\mathrm{J^{-1}}E \qquad (4.12)$$

At 20°C

$$\ln 1.0 = \ln\eta_0 + \frac{E}{1.38 \times 10^{-23}\,\mathrm{J\,K^{-1}} \times 293\,\mathrm{K}}$$

so

$$0.000 = \ln\eta_0 + 2.473 \times 10^{20}\,\mathrm{J^{-1}}E \qquad (4.13)$$

Subtracting Equation (4.13) from Equation (4.12) gives

$$0.875 = E\left(2.560 \times 10^{20} - 2.473 \times 10^{20}\right)\mathrm{J^{-1}}$$

$$= E \times 0.087 \times 10^{20}\,\mathrm{J^{-1}}$$

Therefore

$$E = \frac{0.875}{0.087 \times 10^{20}\,\mathrm{J^{-1}}}$$

$$= 1.006 \times 10^{-19}\,\mathrm{J}$$

(b) Substituting this value of E in Equation (4.13) gives

$$0.000 = \ln\eta_0 + 2.473 \times 10^{20}\,\mathrm{J^{-1}} \times 1.006 \times 10^{-19}\,\mathrm{J}$$

so

$$\ln\eta_0 = -2.473 \times 10^{20}\,\mathrm{J^{-1}} \times 1.006 \times 10^{-19}\,\mathrm{J}$$

$$= -24.88$$

and therefore

$$\eta_0 = e^{-24.88}$$

$$= 1.568 \times 10^{-11}\,\mathrm{Pa\,s}$$

(c) At 373 K

$$\frac{E}{kT} = \frac{1.006 \times 10^{-19}\,\mathrm{J}}{1.38 \times 10^{-23}\,\mathrm{J\,K^{-1}} \times 373\,\mathrm{K}}$$

$$= 19.54$$

so

$$\eta = 1.568 \times 10^{-11}\,\mathrm{Pa\,s} \times e^{19.54}$$

$$= 4.8 \times 10^{-3}\,\mathrm{Pa\,s}$$

Q8

$$R = \frac{\rho v_c r}{\eta}$$

So units of R are

$$\frac{\left(\text{kg m}^{-3}\right)\left(\text{m s}^{-1}\right)\text{m}}{\text{Pa s}} = \frac{\text{kg m}^{-1}\,\text{s}^{-1}}{\text{N m}^{-2}\,\text{s}}$$

$$= \frac{\text{kg m s}^{-2}}{\text{N}}$$

$$= \frac{\text{kg m s}^{-2}}{\text{kg m s}^{-2}}$$

so R is dimensionless.

Q9

(a)

$$v_c = R\frac{\eta}{\rho r}$$

$$= 1000 \times \frac{0.001\,\text{Pa s}}{1000\,\text{kg m}^{-3} \times 6 \times 10^{-3}\,\text{m}}$$

$$= 0.17\,\text{m s}^{-1}$$

(b) Using Equation (4.3) from p. 107 for laminar flow will only give a flow rate of

$$\frac{\Delta V}{\Delta t} = \pi r^2 v$$

$$= \pi \times \left(6 \times 10^{-3}\,\text{m}\right)^2 \times 0.17\,\text{m s}^{-1}$$

$$= 1.9 \times 10^{-5}\ \text{m}^3\,\text{s}^{-1}$$

$$= 19\,\text{cm}^3\,\text{s}^{-1}$$

So, to get a flow rate in excess of 19 cm³ s⁻¹ the flow will need to become turbulent.

Q10

$$\frac{\Delta V}{\Delta t} = \sqrt{\left(\frac{\pi^2 R r^5}{8\rho}\right)\frac{\Delta P}{\Delta l}}$$

so

$$\frac{\Delta P}{\Delta l} = \left(\frac{\Delta V}{\Delta t}\right)^2 \frac{8\rho}{\pi^2 R r^5}$$

A mass flow rate of 1 kg s⁻¹ is the same as a volume flow rate of 1×10^{-3} m³ s⁻¹, therefore

$$\frac{\Delta P}{\Delta l} = \frac{\left(1 \times 10^{-3}\,\text{m}^3\,\text{s}^{-1}\right)^2 \times 8 \times 1000\,\text{kg m}^{-3}}{\pi^2 \times 1000 \times \left(6.5 \times 10^{-3}\,\text{m}\right)^5}$$

$$= 6.99 \times 10^4\ \text{Pa m}^{-1}$$

$$= 7 \times 10^4\ \text{Pa m}^{-1}\ \text{(to one significant figure)}$$

(a head of about 7 m of water).

Q11

(a) Volume flow rate $\dfrac{\Delta V}{\Delta t}$ is simply the volume of liquid that flows in 1 s, so it is 10 cm³ divided by t and converted to m³ s⁻¹.

The pressure gradient $\dfrac{\Delta P}{\Delta l}$ is the pressure calculated from $\rho g h$ divided by the length of the capillary tube

$$\text{pressure gradient} = \frac{1000\,\text{kg m}^{-3} \times 9.81\,\text{m s}^{-2} \times h}{5\,\text{cm}}$$

Columns 3 and 4 of Table 4.3 oveleaf show volume flow rate and pressure gradient. (We have also added a column for the square root of the pressure gradient – you will see why in part (c).)

Table 4.3 Answer to Question 11(a)

h/m	t/s	$\dfrac{\Delta V}{\Delta t}/10^{-6}\,\mathrm{m}^3\,\mathrm{s}^{-1}$	$\dfrac{\Delta P}{\Delta l}/10^5\,\mathrm{Pa}\,\mathrm{m}^{-1}$	$\sqrt{\dfrac{\Delta P}{\Delta l}}/10^2\sqrt{(\mathrm{Pa}\,\mathrm{m}^{-1})}$
0.890	6.46	1.55	1.74	4.18
0.735	6.95	1.44	1.44	3.80
0.575	7.10	1.41	1.13	3.36
0.490	7.85	1.27	0.96	3.10
0.304	10.84	0.92	0.60	2.44
0.200	12.86	0.78	0.39	1.98

(b) The graph of volume flow rate against pressure gradient is shown in Figure 4.20(a). The line of best fit does not pass through the origin so these variables are not directly proportional and Poiseuille's equation is not the one that fits this data. This flow is not laminar.

(c) The square root of the pressure gradient is given in column 5 of Table 4.3. The graph of volume flow rate against the square root of the pressure gradient is shown in Figure 4.20(b). The line of best fit passes through the origin. This means that the volume flow rate is proportional to the square root of the pressure gradient, which tells you that the flow is turbulent.

In order to find R we need to take another look at Equation 4.11

$$\frac{\Delta V}{\Delta t} = \sqrt{\left(\frac{\pi^2 R r^5}{8\rho}\right)\frac{\Delta P}{\Delta l}}$$

and compare it with the equation for a straight line $y = mx + c$

We have plotted $\dfrac{\Delta V}{\Delta t}$ as y and $\sqrt{\dfrac{\Delta P}{\Delta l}}$ as x.

Therefore c is zero and the gradient is

$$m = \sqrt{\left(\frac{\pi^2 R r^5}{8\rho}\right)}$$

Squaring both sides gives

$$m^2 = \frac{\pi^2 R r^5}{8\rho}$$

and rearranging gives

$$R = \frac{8\rho m^2}{\pi^2 r^5}$$

$$= \frac{8 \times 1000\,\mathrm{kg\,m^{-3}} \times \left(4\times10^{-9}\,\mathrm{m^4\,kg^{-1/2}}\right)^2}{\pi^2 \times \left(0.9\times10^{-3}\,\mathrm{m}\right)^5}$$

$$= 21.9$$

Q12

(a)

$$\frac{\Delta V}{\Delta t} = \sqrt{\left(\frac{\pi^2 R r^5}{8\rho}\right)\frac{\Delta P}{\Delta l}}$$

$$= \sqrt{\left(\frac{\pi^2 \times 1000 \times (0.4\,\mathrm{m})^5}{8\times 860\,\mathrm{kg\,m^{-3}}}\right)\times 30\,\mathrm{Pa\,m^{-1}}}$$

$$= \sqrt{\frac{101\,\mathrm{m}^5}{6880\,\mathrm{kg\,m^{-3}}}\times 30\,\mathrm{Pa\,m^{-1}}}$$

$$= 0.66\ \mathrm{m}^3\,\mathrm{s}^{-1} \text{ (to two significant figures)}$$

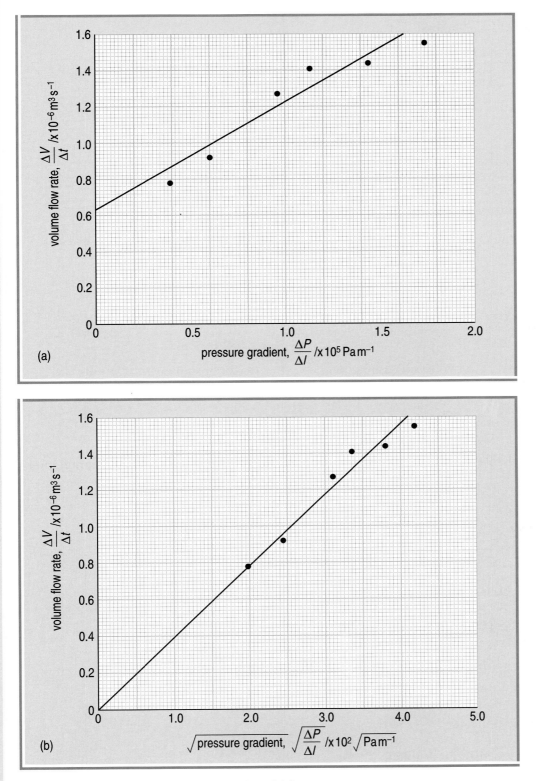

Figure 4.20 Answer to Question 11(b) and (c)

(b)

$$\frac{\Delta V}{\Delta t} = \pi r^2 v$$

so

$$v = \frac{\Delta V/\Delta t}{\pi r^2}$$

$$= \frac{0.66\,\text{m}^3\,\text{s}^{-1}}{\pi \times (0.4\,\text{m})^2}$$

$$= 1.3\,\text{m}\,\text{s}^{-1} \text{ (to two significant figures)}$$

The critical velocity is

$$v_c = \frac{1000\eta}{\rho r}$$

$$= \frac{1000 \times 5.0 \times 10^{-3}\,\text{Pa}\,\text{s}}{860\,\text{kg}\,\text{m}^{-3} \times 0.40\,\text{m}}$$

$$= 1.5 \times 10^{-2}\,\text{m}\,\text{s}^{-1} \text{ (to two significant figures)}$$

v is much larger than v_c, so the flow is definitely turbulent.

(c)

$$\Delta P = 500\,\text{km} \times 30\,000\,\text{Pa}\,\text{km}^{-1}$$

$$= 1.5 \times 10^7\,\text{Pa}$$

transfer efficiency is

$$\frac{\Delta P}{U} = \frac{1.5 \times 10^7\,\text{Pa}}{3.5 \times 10^{10}\,\text{J}\,\text{m}^{-3}}$$

$$= 4.3 \times 10^{-4} \text{ (to two significant figures)}$$

(Remember from Section 3 that it is better to use pumps at regular intervals in a pipeline.)

(d) The pressure gradient must be quadrupled to double the flow rate since the flow rate is proportional to $\sqrt{\dfrac{\Delta P}{\Delta l}}$. So the transfer efficiency is also quadrupled, becoming

$$4 \times \left(4.3 \times 10^{-4}\right) = 1.7 \times 10^{-3}$$

Q13

(a) The critical velocity is

$$v_c = \frac{1000\eta}{\rho r}$$

$$= \frac{1000 \times 0.001\,\text{Pa}\,\text{s}}{1000\,\text{kg}\,\text{m}^{-3} \times 1.625\,\text{m}}$$

$$= 6.15 \times 10^{-4}\,\text{m}\,\text{s}^{-1}$$

(to three significant figures)

So the volume flow rate at this velocity is

$$\frac{\Delta V}{\Delta t} = \pi r^2 v$$

$$= \pi \times (1.625\,\text{m})^2 \times 6.15 \times 10^{-4}\,\text{m}\,\text{s}^{-1}$$

$$= 5.10 \times 10^{-3}\,\text{m}^3\,\text{s}^{-1}$$

(to three significant figures)

(b)

$$P_{\text{out}} = 1.2 \times 10^6\,\text{J}\,\text{m}^{-3} \times 5.1 \times 10^{-3}\,\text{m}^3\,\text{s}^{-1}$$

$$= 6.1 \times 10^3\,\text{W} \text{ (to two significant figures)}$$

(c)

$$\frac{\Delta V}{\Delta t} = \frac{\pi r^4}{8\eta} \frac{\Delta P}{\Delta l}$$

so

$$\frac{\Delta P}{\Delta l} = \frac{\Delta V/\Delta t}{\pi r^4/8\eta}$$

$$= \frac{5.10 \times 10^{-3}\,\text{m}^3\,\text{s}^{-1}}{\pi \times (1.625\,\text{m})^4 / 8 \times 0.001\,\text{Pa}\,\text{s}}$$

$$= 1.86 \times 10^{-6}\,\text{Pa}\,\text{m}^{-1}$$

(to three significant figures)

Pressure drop is given by

$$\Delta P = 1.86 \times 10^{-6} \, \text{Pa}\,\text{m}^{-1} \times \Delta l$$

$$= 1.86 \times 10^{-6} \, \text{Pa}\,\text{m}^{-1} \times 1.2 \times 10^{3} \, \text{m}$$

$$= 2.232 \times 10^{-3} \, \text{Pa}$$

$$= 2.2 \times 10^{-3} \, \text{Pa}$$

(to two significant figures)

This is also the work done in transporting 1 m³ of water through the pipe (see Equation 3.2 on page 72). So the work done transporting each 1 m³ through the pipe is 2.2×10^{-3} J.

(d) Transfer efficiency is

$$\frac{2.232 \times 10^{-3} \, \text{J}\,\text{m}^{-3}}{1.2 \times 10^{6} \, \text{J}\,\text{m}^{-3}} = 1.9 \times 10^{-9}$$

(to two significant figures)

This is an extremely good figure, so you can easily afford to increase the power output of the system by going turbulent!

Q14

(a)

$$\frac{\Delta V}{\Delta t} = \frac{50 \, \text{MW}}{1.2 \, \text{MJ}}$$

$$= 42 \, \text{m}^{3}\,\text{s}^{-1} \quad \text{(to two significant figures)}$$

(b)

$$\left(\frac{\Delta V}{\Delta t}\right)^{2} = \frac{\pi^{2} R r^{5}}{8\rho} \frac{\Delta P}{\Delta l}$$

$$\frac{\Delta P}{\Delta l} = \frac{\left(\dfrac{\Delta V}{\Delta t}\right)^{2}}{\left(\dfrac{\pi^{2} R r^{5}}{8\rho}\right)}$$

$$= \frac{\left(42 \, \text{m}^{3}\,\text{s}^{-1}\right)^{2}}{\left(\dfrac{\pi^{2} \times 1000 \times \left(1.625 \, \text{m}\right)^{5}}{8 \times 1000 \, \text{kg}\,\text{m}^{-3}}\right)}$$

$$= 3.01 \, \text{Pa}\,\text{m}^{-1}$$

$$\Delta P = 3.01 \, \text{Pa}\,\text{m}^{-1} \times l$$

$$= 3.01 \, \text{Pa}\,\text{m}^{-1} \times 1.2 \times 10^{3} \, \text{m}$$

$$= 3.6 \times 10^{3} \, \text{Pa}$$

(to two significant figures)

This is also the work done in transporting 1 m³ of water through the pipe (see Equation 3.2 on p. 72). So the work done transporting each 1 m³ through the pipe is 3.6×10^{-3} J.

$$\text{transfer efficiency} = \frac{3.6 \times 10^{3} \, \text{J}\,\text{m}^{-3}}{1.2 \times 10^{6} \, \text{J}\,\text{m}^{-3}}$$

$$= 3.01 \times 10^{-3}$$

(to two significant figures)

This is a million times larger, but it is still low and is fairly acceptable.

5

We are all used to seeing liquids flow through open channels. Rivers, streams and canals are all common in our landscape. We also use open channels for irrigation, drainage and in industrial processes such as waterworks and effluent treatment plants.

You may have seen a weir. These are walls placed across a river or stream either to increase the depth upstream, perhaps to improve the habitat, or to regulate the flow of water as the river level changes (you will often see a weir next to a lock on a river). Water builds up behind the weir until it flows over. After heavy rain the water will rush over the weir and in drought it will just trickle over. The water level upstream will depend on the rate of flow of water and we can use this fact to help us develop a simple method of measuring the rate of flow indirectly.

We will begin Section 5 by investigating this method of measuring flow.

READY TO STUDY TEST

Before you begin this section you should be able to:

■ use the equation for kinetic energy

$$E_\mathrm{k} = \frac{1}{2} mv^2$$

and for gravitational potential energy

$$E_\mathrm{pot} = mgh$$

■ use trigonometric functions

■ interpret straight-line graphs.

QUESTIONS

R1 A rock fall causes a pulse of water to move down a narrow channel at 4 m s^{-1}. The pulse of water has a mass of 250 kg. What is its kinetic energy?

R2 The pulse of water in R1 flows over a waterfall 15 m high. How much kinetic energy has it gained from this drop in gravitational potential energy?

R3 What is (a) the cosine of 60°, (b) the angle with a sine of 0.86603?

R4 A straight-line graph has a gradient of 0.8 and the line crosses the y-axis at $y = 2.0$. Write out the equation of the line.

Weir

Irrigation channels

5.1 Measuring liquid flow in an open channel

In waterworks and effluent treatment plants, flow rates in open channels often have to be measured. This is usually done by measuring the height of the liquid's surface above some particular level as it flows over a weir. The meters used for this are simple devices that can be readily adapted for continuous measurement. A float connected to a variable resistor, often called a **sender unit**, is all that is needed. This system is also used in many fuel tanks, where it measures depth directly rather than being calibrated for flow.

Sewage treatment plant

Developing an expression for the rate of flow in these cases requires the use of calculus. If you have not dealt with calculus, ignore the theory below and go straight to Exploration 5.1. We will repeat the important equations when you need to use them.

Some theory

The water before the weir is effectively still, so we can consider the speeding up of the flow as it goes over the weir to be due to a transfer from gravitational potential energy to kinetic energy.

> Consider a tiny mass of water m that falls from a height h. How much gravitational potential energy is transferred by its fall?

Gravitational potential energy transfer is given by

$$E_{\text{pot}} = \text{mass} \times \text{gravitational field strength} \times \text{vertical height of fall}$$

$$= mgh$$

 This tiny mass had no kinetic energy before its fall, but moves at a speed v afterwards. Write an expression for the amount of kinetic energy that must have been transferred to it.

Kinetic energy is given by

$$E_{\text{k}} = \frac{1}{2} \times \text{mass} \times \text{speed}^2$$

$$= \frac{1}{2}mv^2$$

 Write an expression linking these two energy transfers together.

As all of the gravitational potential energy is transferred to kinetic energy

$$mgh = \frac{1}{2}mv^2$$

 Hence obtain an expression for the speed of flow v.

Dividing both sides of the equation by m we have

$$gh = \frac{1}{2}v^2$$

so

$$v^2 = 2gh$$

and

$$v = \sqrt{2gh} \tag{5.1}$$

(*Note*: In reality the speed will be less than this because of energy transfers within the water caused by viscosity and surface tension.)

Now, imagine the flow over the weir is extremely low so that the water only just maintains a very small depth dh over the top of the weir, as shown in Figure 5.1. Using the relationship for v above (Equation 5.1), we can now develop an equation for the volume flow rate over the weir.

 The width of the weir is W and its height is H. Write an expression for the volume of water flowing over the weir each second.

Volume per second = area of section

$$\times \text{length passing over weir each second}$$

$$= Wdh \times \sqrt{2gH}$$

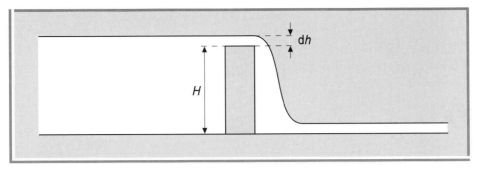

Figure 5.1   A weir

This expression is true only when the flow is extremely low. It turns out that the general relationship for volume flow rate over a weir is

$$\frac{\Delta V}{\Delta t} = \frac{2}{3}W\sqrt{2gH^3}$$

Allowing for the effects mentioned earlier, and a narrowing of the stream as it flows over the weir, a correction factor, the coefficient of discharge C_D, is incorporated to give

$$\frac{\Delta V}{\Delta t} = \frac{2}{3}C_D W\sqrt{2g}H^{3/2} \tag{5.2}$$

A variation on this method of measuring flow rate uses the **vee-notch** weir, as shown in Figure 5.2 (ignore the shaded area and labelling for the moment). Here the channel is blocked with a barrier that has a triangular 'vee' section cut out from it, so the fluid flows through the vee rather than over the top of the barrier. This effectively produces a flow meter with a variable sensitivity.

◆ How does the sensitivity of a vee-notch weir vary with flow rate?

At low flow rates the gap is narrow. At higher flow rates the water passes through wider sections. This means that at higher flow rates the depth of the water increases more slowly than if the slot were the same width all the way up.

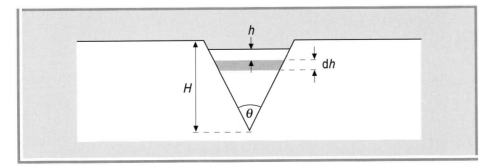

Figure 5.2
A vee-notch weir

We can develop a similar argument for volume flow rate through a vee-notch as the one we developed above for an ordinary weir. Look again at Figure 5.2. The vee-notch has an angle of θ, the water surface is a height H above the base of the notch and the tiny shaded element of depth dh is h below the surface.

 Write an expression for the volume of water flowing each second through the shaded section.

Again it is area of the shaded strip × speed of flow.

The width, W, of the shaded section can be worked out using Figure 5.3:

$$\tan\frac{\theta}{2} = \frac{W/2}{H-h}$$

Rearranging, we have

$$W = 2(H-h)\tan\frac{\theta}{2}$$

So the area is

$$W \times dh = 2(H-h)\tan\frac{\theta}{2} \times dh$$

Therefore, volume flow rate is

$$\frac{\Delta V}{\Delta t} = \left(2(H-h)\tan\frac{\theta}{2} \times dh\right) \times \sqrt{2gh}$$

Using the advanced technique of integration this becomes

$$\frac{\Delta V}{\Delta t} = \frac{8}{15}\tan\frac{\theta}{2}\sqrt{2g}\,H^{5/2}$$

And with the correction factor of the coefficient of discharge we have

$$\frac{\Delta V}{\Delta t} = \frac{8}{15}C_D\tan\frac{\theta}{2}\sqrt{2g}\,H^{5/2} \tag{5.3}$$

A similar argument provides an expression for the rate of flow through an orifice (hole) with a sharp edge:

$$\frac{\Delta V}{\Delta t} = 0.25C_D\pi d^2\sqrt{2gH} \tag{5.4}$$

where d is the diameter of the orifice and H is the height of the water level above the centre of the orifice.

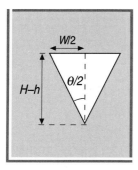
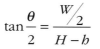

Figure 5.3
Working out the width of the shaded section in the vee-notch meter

E Exploration 5.1 Measuring flow with a vee-notch meter

Apparatus:

◆ Marley plastic guttering, 1.5 m long with one end stopped up ◆ two vee-notches of different angles ◆ water pump ◆ cold feed and expansion tank ◆ measuring jug ◆ stopwatch ◆ small ruler

Vee-notches are often used to measure volume flow rates over weirs in open channels. As the liquid flows along the channel it tends to rise at the notch: the height of the liquid above the base of the notch can be used to calculate the flow rate.

Using some simple physics and a little calculus can show that the flow rate through a vee-notch is given by

$$\frac{\Delta V}{\Delta t} = \frac{8}{15} C_D \tan\frac{\theta}{2} \sqrt{2g} H^{5/2}$$

(Equation 5.3)

where θ is the angle of the notch, H is the height of the liquid in the notch above the base of the vee, g is the gravitational field strength (9.81 N kg^{-1}) and C_D is a correction coefficient known as the coefficient of discharge, which is introduced to allow for the effects of surface tension, roughness of the surfaces, viscosity and a narrowing of the stream as it flows through the notch.

Set up the equipment as shown in Figure 5.4.

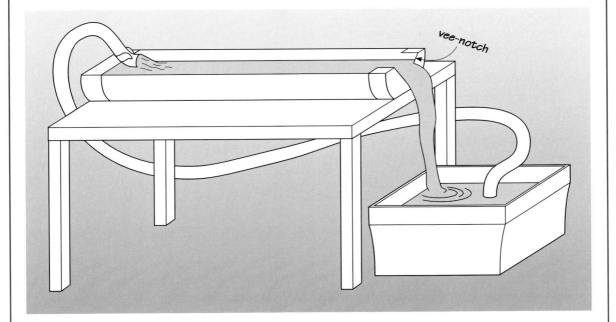

vee-notch

Figure 5.4 Using a vee-notch meter

Fill the tank with about 12 litres of water. Some tanks have a ridge in them at about the 12 litre level. If yours is like this, fill to the ridge.

Fit one of the vee-notches to the outflow end of the guttering and position this just above the tank.

Run the piping from the pump and fix it in its holder above the closed end of the guttering. Ensure that the guttering is level.

Draw up a table of results like Table 5.1.

height H of water above base of vee/mm	time to collect 1 litre of water/s				average flow rate/litre s^{-1}
	first	second	third	average	

Table 5.1
Table of results for Exploration 5.1

Switch on the pump and adjust it to give the slowest flow rate. The adjuster is attached to the pump itself, so you will get your hands wet. Let the system settle for a few minutes so that the height H of the water above the base of the vee stabilizes.

Measure the height of the water in the vee-notch above the base of the vee and note this in the table. Now record the time taken to collect 1 litre of water from the outflow. Do this three times, adding your results to the table on each occasion. Calculate the average time taken to collect 1 litre of water.

Alter the flow adjuster on the pump and obtain at least two more sets of collection times for 1 litre of water and the associated heights H of the water above the base of the vee-notch.

Calculate the average flow rate (litre s^{-1}). This is done by calculating the reciprocal of the collection time. Hence, if 1 litre of water was collected in an average of 5.9 seconds, the average flow rate would be $\dfrac{1}{5.9} = 0.17$ litre s^{-1}.

Repeat the investigation using a vee-notch with a different angle. Then switch off the pump.

Use your results to see if the flow rate for each vee-notch is proportional to H and obtain an average value for the correction coefficient C_D for each notch.

Q1 Is the correction coefficient different when you use a vee-notch with a different angle? ◆

Q2 Sets of results obtained using vee-notches of $\theta = 90°$ and $\theta = 53°$ are shown in Tables 5.2 and 5.3.

Table 5.2 90° vee-notch

Height H of water above base of vee/$\times 10^{-3}$ m	Average flow rate/ $\times 10^{-3}$ m^{3}s^{-1}	$H^{5/2}/\times 10^{-6}$ m$^{5/2}$
8.000	0.006	5.700
13.000	0.024	19.300
24.000	0.117	89.200

Table 5.3 53° vee-notch

Height H of water above base of vee/$\times 10^{-3}$ m	Average flow rate/ $\times 10^{-3}$ m^{3}s^{-1}	$H^{5/2}/\times 10^{-6}$ m$^{5/2}$
13.000	0.028	19.300
22.000	0.067	71.800
27.000	0.116	119.800

(a) For the 90° vee-notch:

(i) Plot a graph of average flow rate against $H^{5/2}$.

(ii) Does your graph show that the average flow rate is directly proportional to $H^{5/2}$? Explain this.

(iii) Using the gradient of your graph, calculate the average value for C_D for these readings.

(b) For the 53° vee-notch:

(i) Plot a graph of average flow rate against $H^{5/2}$.

(ii) Does your graph show that the average flow rate is directly proportional to $H^{5/2}$? Explain this.

(iii) Using the gradient of your graph, calculate the average value for C_D for these readings.

(c) Do your results show that the value of C_D is fixed, or is it dependent on the angle of the vee-notch? ◆

For cheapness, a device called an **orifice plate** can be placed inside a pipeline and the difference between the pressures on either side of it can be used to calculate the flow rate. These orifice plates can also be used with open channels, as in Exploration 5.2.

E ▶ Exploration 5.2 Measuring liquid flow with a sharp-edged orifice

Apparatus:

- ◆ Marley plastic guttering, 1.5 m long with one end stopped up
- ◆ three orifice plates with holes of different diameters, each with a Velcro pad attached ◆ water pump ◆ cold feed and expansion tank ◆ measuring jug
- ◆ stopwatch ◆ small ruler with Velcro pad attached

When orifice plates are used to determine flow rates in open channels, the height of the liquid above the centre of the orifice is one of the factors involved in the calculation.

Using some simple physics and a little calculus can show that the flow rate through a sharp-edged orifice is given by:

$$\frac{\Delta V}{\Delta t} = 0.25 C_D \pi d^2 \sqrt{2gH}$$

(Equation 5.4)

where d is the diameter of the orifice, H is the height of the liquid above the centre of the orifice, g is the gravitational field strength (9.81 N kg^{-1}) and C_D is a correction coefficient known as the coefficient of discharge, which is introduced to allow for the effects of surface tension, roughness of the surfaces, viscosity and a narrowing of the stream as it flows out of the orifice.

Set up the equipment as shown in Figure 5.5.

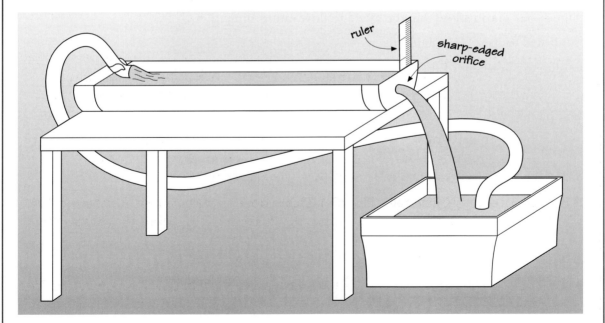

Figure 5.5 Apparatus for Exploration 5.2

Fill the tank with about 12 litres of water. Some tanks have a ridge in them at about the 12 litre level. If yours is like this, fill to the ridge.

Fit one of the orifice plates to the outflow end of the guttering and position this just above the tank.

Fix the ruler with the Velcro pad on it to the pad inside the orifice plate. Adjust its position so that its zero is on the line marking the centre of the orifice.

Run the piping from the pump and fix it in its holder above the closed end of the guttering. Ensure that the guttering is level.

Draw up a table of results like Table 5.4.

height H of water above centre of orifice/mm	time to collect 1 litre of water/s				average flow rate/litre s^{-1}
	first	second	third	average	

Table 5.4
Table of results for Exploration 5.2

Switch on the pump and adjust it to give a slow flow rate, but one that ensures that the orifice is covered by water. The adjuster is attached to the pump itself, so you will get your hands wet. Let the system settle for a few minutes so that the height H of the water above the centre of the orifice stabilizes.

Measure the height of the water above the centre of the orifice and note this in the table. Now record the time taken to collect 1 litre of water from the outflow. Do this three times, adding your results to the table on each occasion. Calculate the average time taken to collect 1 litre of water.

Alter the flow adjuster on the pump and obtain at least two more sets of collection times for 1 litre of water and the associated heights H of the water above the centre of the orifice.

Calculate the average flow rate (litre s^{-1}). This is done by calculating the reciprocal of the collection time. Hence, if 1 litre of water was collected in an average of 5.9 seconds,

the average flow rate would be $\dfrac{1}{5.9} = 0.17 \, \text{litre s}^{-1}$.

Repeat the investigations with the other orifice plates with different diameter holes. Then switch off the pump.

Use your results to see if the flow rate for each orifice plate is proportional to d^2 and obtain an average value for the correction coefficient C_D for each orifice.

Q3 Does the correction coefficient C_D change with different values of d, the diameter of the orifice? ◆

Q4 Sets of results obtained using orifices of two different diameters are shown in Tables 5.5 and 5.6.

Table 5.5 Diameter $d = 13$ mm

Height H of water above centre of orifice/$\times 10^{-3}$ m	Average flow rate/ $\times 10^{-3}$ m^{3}s^{-1}	$d^2 \sqrt{H}/\times 10^{-5}$ m
6.000	0.034	1.31
14.000	0.056	2.00
29.000	0.078	2.88

Table 5.6 Diameter $d = 16$ mm

Height H of water above centre of orifice/$\times 10^{-3}$ m	Average flow rate/ $\times 10^{-3}$ m^{3}s^{-1}	$d^2 \sqrt{H}/\times 10^{-5}$ m
11.000	0.074	2.68
16.000	0.087	3.24
28.000	0.130	4.28

(a) For the 13 mm diameter orifice:

(i) Plot a graph of average flow rate against $d^2 \sqrt{H}$.

(ii) Does your graph show that the average flow rate is directly proportional to $d^2 \sqrt{H}$? Explain this.

(iii) Using the gradient of your graph, calculate an average value for C_D for these readings.

(b) For the 16 mm diameter orifice:

(i) Plot a graph of average flow rate against $d^2 \sqrt{H}$.

(ii) Does your graph show that the average flow rate is directly proportional to $d^2 \sqrt{H}$? Explain this.

(iii) Using the gradient of your graph, calculate an average value for C_D for these readings.

(c) Do your results show that the value of C_D is fixed, or is it dependent on the size of the orifice? ◆

5.2 Vortex-shedding flow meters

One of the most widely used type of flow meter is the vortex-shedding flow meter. This makes use of the fact that when a non-streamlined object is placed in a pipeline or open channel and fluid flows past it, vortices or eddies are produced. The faster the speed of flow the more vortices are produced each second.

These are known as Kármán vortices after Theodore von Kármán (1881–1963), the Hungarian-born physicist and aeronautical engineer who discovered the effect. He worked for much of his life in the USA and was instrumental in developing that country's aerospace industry. Vortices such as these were responsible for putting the Tacoma Narrows suspension bridge into oscillation and bringing about its collapse (you will have met this example if you have studied the SLIPP unit *Physics, Jazz and Pop*). Similar effects would be produced around some chimneys if they did not have vortex shedders fitted to them. Huge natural vortices like the ones shown in the photograph can be seen on Earth when it is observed from space.

One common method of detecting vortices in pipes or channels uses a heated thermistor. As each vortex passes the thermistor, the rate of transfer of energy to the fluid from the thermistor changes and so the temperature of the thermistor changes. As with a hot-wire anemometer, when the temperature of a thermistor changes so does its resistance. Unfortunately, it is not easy to make equipment for use in schools and colleges that is sensitive enough to be able to detect such vortices automatically. Hence there are no explorations of this technique for you to deal with directly. However, we would hope that you might get a chance to see one of these devices in use in industry.

Q5 Outline some other methods that could be used to detect vortices. ◆

Chimney with vortex shedder

Vortices produced in the cloud downwind of Guadalupe island, Mexico. These extend over 150 miles.

The results in Tables 5.7 and 5.8 were obtained from a vortex-shedding flow meter measuring the speed of oil flow in a pipeline. The first obstacle's width was 10 mm and the second had a width of 5.0 mm.

Tables 5.7 Measurements made for an obstacle 10 mm wide

Speed of flow/m s^{-1}	Frequency of vortices/Hz
0.5	10
1.0	21
1.5	31
2.0	42
2.5	53
5.0	110

Tables 5.8 Measurements made for an obstacle 5.0 mm wide

Speed of flow/m s^{-1}	Frequency of vortices/Hz
0.5	20
1.0	41
1.5	63
2.0	83
2.5	105
5.0	222

 What is the relationship between speed of flow and the frequency of the vortices?

Figure 5.6 shows that the frequency of the vortices is proportional to the speed of flow

$$f \propto v$$

 What effect does halving the width of the obstacle in the pipeline have on the frequency of the vortices?

By comparing the two lines of best fit in Figure 5.6 we can see that, for any speed, halving the width of the obstacle doubles the frequency. So frequency is inversely proportional to width.

$$f \propto \frac{1}{L}$$

where L is the width of obstacle.

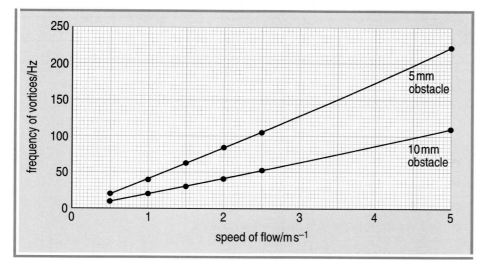

Figure 5.6
Frequency of vortices versus speed of flow for different sized obstacles

Putting these two pieces of information together gives us this relationship

$$f \propto \frac{v}{L}$$

and therefore

$$f = S\frac{v}{L} \tag{5.5}$$

where S is a constant that we call the Strouhal number.

Q6 (a) Use Equation (5.5) to calculate values of the Strouhal number for the flow meter and liquid that gave the results in Table 5.7.

(b) Use Equation (5.5) to calculate values of the Strouhal number for the flow meter and liquid that gave the results in Table 5.8.

(c) Does the Strouhal number vary with different obstacle sizes? ◆

There are many other methods of measuring the flow of both liquids and gases besides those we have covered here. If you have time, you could research some of those that we have not dealt with and present a report to your group. Other methods of measuring flow include:

- Doppler ultrasound meter
- Doppler laser meter
- swirlmeter
- vibrating tube or Coriolis effect meter.

You can probably think of others.

Alternatively, you could go and see some flow meters in use. Find out which types of flow meters are used and why they have been chosen for the particular job that they do.

Industries and institutions that you could visit to see the measurement of flow in practice include:

- power stations
- car factories
- pump manufacturers
- hospitals
- water supply plants
- washing machine manufacturers
- petrol stations.

Achievements

After working through this section you should be able to:

- explain how a vee-notch meter is used to measure liquid flow and give examples of situations in which it may be useful

- use the equation for flow through a vee-notch: $\dfrac{\Delta V}{\Delta t} = \dfrac{8}{15} C_D \tan\dfrac{\theta}{2}\sqrt{2g}\,H^{5/2}$

- describe the action of an orifice meter

- use the equation for flow through a sharp-edged orifice:

$$\frac{\Delta V}{\Delta t} = 0.25 C_D \pi d^2 \sqrt{2gH}$$

- explain the principle behind a vortex-shedding flow meter

- use the equation relating frequency of vortices to speed of flow and width of obstacle in a vortex-shedding flow meter: $f = S\dfrac{v}{L}$.

Glossary

Sender unit   A piece of equipment incorporating a sensor that is designed to send a signal (a variable voltage) to a gauge located somewhere else.

Vee-notch   A section cut out of a plain barrier in the shape of a V so that fluid held back by the barrier is allowed through the vee-notch.

Orifice plate   A plain barrier with a sharp-edged hole cut out of it so that fluid held back by the barrier is allowed through the hole.

Answers to Ready to Study questions

R1

$$E_k = \frac{1}{2}mv^2$$
$$= \frac{1}{2} \times 250\,\text{kg} \times \left(4\,\text{ms}^{-1}\right)^2$$
$$= \frac{1}{2} \times 250\,\text{kg} \times \left(4\,\text{ms}^{-1}\right)^2$$
$$= 2000\,\text{J}$$

R2

$$E_{\text{pot}} = mgh$$
$$= 250\,\text{kg} \times 9.81\,\text{ms}^{-1} \times 15\,\text{m}$$
$$= 3.7 \times 10^3\,\text{J}$$

R3

(a) 0.5.

(b) 60°.

R4

The equation for a straight line is

$$y = mx + c$$

where m is the gradient and c is the point where the line crosses the y-axis.

In this case $m = 0.8$ and $c = 2.0$, so the equation of the line is

$$y = 0.8x + 2.0$$

Answers to questions in the text

Q1

Yes. The correction coefficient is dependent on the angle of the vee-notch as this has a marked effect on many other factors.

Q2

(a) (i) See Figure 5.7(a).

(ii) It is directly proportional: the line is straight and it passes through the origin. It would have been better to have a few extra plots to make sure.

(iii) The gradient of the graph is

$$\frac{\text{average flow rate}}{H^{5/2}}$$

Rearranging Equation (5.3) you can see that

$$\frac{\text{average flow rate}}{H^{5/2}} = \frac{8}{15} C_D \tan\frac{\theta}{2}\sqrt{2g}$$

so we have

$$1.29\,\text{m}^{1/2}\,\text{s}^{-1} = \frac{8}{15} C_D \tan 45°\sqrt{2 \times 9.81\,\text{ms}^{-2}}$$

giving

$$C_D = \frac{15 \times 1.29\,\text{m}^{1/2}\,\text{s}^{-1}}{8 \times 1 \times 4.429\,\text{m}^{1/2}\,\text{s}^{-1}}$$

$$= 0.55 \text{ (to two significant figures)}$$

(b) (i) See Figure 5.7(b).

(ii) There is rather more uncertainty in the results here, but it looks as if we again have direct proportionality, with a straight line passing through the origin. Again, it would have been helpful to have a few extra plots.

(iii) The gradient of the graph is

$$\frac{\text{average flow rate}}{H^{5/2}} = \frac{8}{15} C_D \tan\frac{\theta}{2}\sqrt{2g}$$

so we have

$$1.02\,\text{m}^{1/2}\,\text{s}^{-1} = \frac{8}{15} C_D \tan 26.5°\sqrt{19.62\,\text{ms}^{-2}}$$

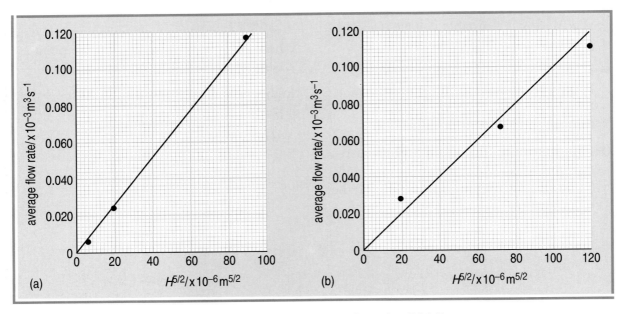

Figure 5.7 (a) Answer to Question 2(a)(i). (b) Answer to Question 2(b)(i)

giving

$$C_D = \frac{15 \times 1.02\,\text{m}^{1/2}\,\text{s}^{-1}}{8 \times 0.499 \times 4.429\,\text{m}^{1/2}\,\text{s}^{-1}}$$

$$= 0.87 \text{ (to two significant figures)}$$

(c) C_D is not fixed. It depends on the angle of the vee-notch.

Q3

Yes. It is likely to be quite different as the diameter of the orifice has a marked effect on many other factors.

Q4

(a) (i) See Figure 5.8(a).

(ii) It does appear to be directly proportional: the line is straight and it passes through the origin. It would have been better to have a few extra plots to make sure.

(iii) The gradient of the graph is

$$\frac{\text{average flow rate}}{d^2\sqrt{H}}$$

Rearranging Equation (5.4) you can see that

$$\frac{\text{average flow rate}}{d^2\sqrt{H}} = 0.25 C_D \pi \sqrt{2g}$$

So we have

$$2.75\,\text{m}^{1/2}\,\text{s}^{-1} = 0.25 C_D \pi \sqrt{2 \times 9.81\,\text{m}\,\text{s}^{-2}}$$

Giving

$$C_D = \frac{2.75\,\text{m}^{1/2}\,\text{s}^{-1}}{0.25\pi \times 4.249\,\text{m}^{1/2}\,\text{s}^{-1}}$$

$$= 0.82 \text{ (to two significant figures)}$$

(b) (i) See Figure 5.8(b).

(ii) The graph tends towards being a straight line through the origin and hence would be showing direct proportionality. However, some extra plots, particularly at low values of average flow rate, would be helpful.

(iii) The gradient of the graph is

$$\frac{\text{average flow rate}}{d^2\sqrt{H}} = 0.25 C_D \pi \sqrt{2g}$$

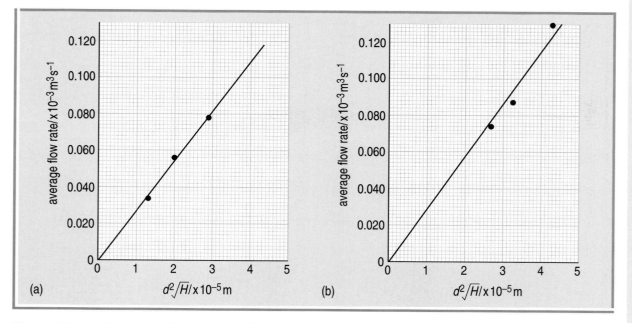

Figure 5.8 (a) Answer to Question 4(a)(i). (b) Answer to Question 4(b)(i)

so we have

$$2.80\,\mathrm{m}^{1/2}\,\mathrm{s}^{-1} = 0.25C_\mathrm{D}\pi\sqrt{2\times9.81\mathrm{m}\,\mathrm{s}^{-2}}$$

giving

$$C_\mathrm{D} = \frac{2.80\,\mathrm{m}^{1/2}\,\mathrm{s}^{-1}}{0.25\pi\times4.249\,\mathrm{m}^{1/2}\,\mathrm{s}^{-1}}$$

$$= 0.84 \text{ (to two significant figures)}$$

(c) It is not fixed but is dependent on the diameter of the orifice. The larger the diameter, the nearer C_D is to 1.

Q5

We hope that you included such sensors as those for detecting pressure, movement and oscillation, but there are many others.

Q6

(a) $f = S\dfrac{v}{L}$

so the Strouhal number is given by

$$S = f\frac{L}{v}$$

If you take the data for a speed of flow of 1 m s^{-1} for an obstacle of width 10 mm (from Table 5.7) you will get

$$S = 21\,\mathrm{Hz}\times\frac{10\times10^{-3}\,\mathrm{m}}{1.0\,\mathrm{m}\,\mathrm{s}^{-1}}$$

$$= 0.21$$

If you do this for all the data in Table 5.7 you will get very similar results.

(b) Turning to Table 5.8 (obstacle width 5.0 mm) and again taking the data for a speed of flow of 1 m s^{-1} you get a value for the Strouhal number of

$$S = 41\,\mathrm{Hz}\times\frac{5.0\times10^{-3}\,\mathrm{m}}{1.0\,\mathrm{m}\,\mathrm{s}^{-1}}$$

$$= 0.205$$

$$= 0.21 \text{ (to two significant figures)}$$

Doing the same for all the data in Table 5.8 again yields very similar results.

(c) The values obtained from the two tables are almost identical, which suggests that the Strouhal number does not depend on the obstacle size.

If you think back to the beginning of this unit, you will realize what a lot of physics you have covered through looking at fluid flow.

To help you to appreciate how far you have come, look back through the list of achievements for each section. If you feel unsure about any of them, go over the relevant section(s) of this unit again. When you feel fairly confident about most of these achievements ask your tutor for the exit test for this unit. When you have done the test, consult your tutor, who has the answers and will probably wish to go through them with you. We hope you have enjoyed learning about the physics of flow with this supported learning unit, and that you want to use more units in the series.

6

CONCLUSION

Further reading and resources

Advanced Assignments Packs 1 and 2 (Part 2 July 1995) Nuffield Science in Practice. Heinemann Educational, Oxford. Advanced GNVQ Science assignments.

Advanced Student Book (1995) Nuffield Science in Practice. Heinemann Educational, Oxford. Student support text for Advanced GNVQ Science.

Allen, J. E. (1986) *Aerodynamics – the science of air in motion*. Allen Brothers and Father, Blythburgh. The definitive text on this subject.

Atkinson, J. K. (1989) *Transducers*. NEMEC, University of Southampton.

Bannister, B. R. and Whitehead, D. G. (1986) *Transducers and Interfacing – principles and techniques*. Van Nostrand, Basingstoke.

Barclay, A. W. and Gibbons, J. A. (n.d.) *Physics Principles at Work*. BP Education Service. This provides a number of methods of measuring flow rates, position and other associated parameters.

Bass, H. G. (1971) *Introduction to Engineering Measurements*. McGraw Hill, London. This has a very straightforward chapter on flow and viscosity, and is very useful for details of how a wide range of measurements are made.

Bishop, O. N. (1991) *Practical Electronic Sensors*. Bernard Babani, London. This gives full details of the physics of various sensors and how they can be interfaced.

Boxer, G. (1988) *Work Out Fluid Mechanics*. Macmillan Work Out Series, Macmillan Education, Basingstoke. A very sound text with developed theory and lots of worked examples.

Brindley, K. (1988) *Sensors and Transducers*. Heinemann Professional Publishing, Oxford. This has very clear details indeed – an excellent text.

Bryan, G. T. (1970) *Control Systems for Technicians*, 2nd edn. Hodder and Stoughton, Sevenoaks. A good introduction to sensors, control and interfacing.

Faraday, M. *Experimental Researches in Electricity*. Michael Faraday's great life work, containing articles published in *Philosophical Transactions* over a span of 40 years. Republished in 1965.

Fox, J. A. (1974) *An Introduction to Engineering Fluid Mechanics*. Macmillan Press, Basingstoke. Very comprehensive indeed. Aimed at undergraduates and HNC/D students but a useful reference for teachers.

Hannah, J. and Hillier, M. J. (1995) *Applied Mechanics*, 3rd edn. Longman Scientific and Technical, Harlow. An excellent support text on the whole of this topic, together with worked examples and many problems to tackle.

Hayward, A. T. J. (1979) *Flowmeters: a basic guide and source-book for users*. Macmillan Press, Basingstoke. The definitive text on this topic.

Intermediate Assignments Pack 1 and 2 (Part 2 July 1995). Nuffield Science in Practice. Heinemann Educational, Oxford. Intermediate GNVQ Science assignments.

Intermediate Student Book (1994). Nuffield Science in Practice. Heinemann Educational, Oxford. Student support text for Intermediate GNVQ Science.

Loxton, R. and Pope, P. (eds) (1986) *Instrumentation – a reader*. Open University text for the course T292 *Instrumentation*. This has an excellent collection of articles on sensors and flow measurement, among many others. Most are reprints from *The Journal of Physics E, Scientific Instruments* and *Measurement and Control*.

Millar, R. (ed.) (n.d.) *Science Activities for A-level. Some ideas for using the laboratory gas meter in advanced school science*. British Gas Education. This provides a number of methods of measuring flow rates together with details of the associated equipment and worked examples.

Nicholl, B. (ed.) (1980) *Physics at Work: a resource book for teachers*. BP Education Service, London, and the Association for Science Education, Hatfield. This has many examples of measuring flow rates and position, but also details some simple experimental work on electrostatic safety in transportation.

Nicholl, B. (ed.) (1982) *The GASS Book. Gas applications for school science*. British Gas Education and the Association for Science Education, London. This provides a number of methods of measuring flow rates together with details of the associated equipment and worked examples.

Noltingk, B. E. (ed.) (1995) *Instrumentation Reference Book*. Butterworths, London. This has very useful chapter on methods of measuring fluid flow. It is a public library reference text.

Ower, E. and Pankhurst, R. C. (1977) *The Measurement of Air Flow*. Pergamon Press, Oxford. The definitive text on this subject for teachers, not for students.

Physics Pack for Advanced GNVQ (1995). Collins Educational, London. Advanced GNVQ Physics resources.

Ramsey, D. C. (1984) *Engineering Instrumentation and Control*. Stanley Thornes, Cheltenham. A very good introduction to sensors, choosing them, how they work. It even has some model investigations to do.

SATIS 16–19. The Association for Science Education, Hatfield. Many related units worthy of attention: 23 *Stick or Slip*, 47 *Playing Safe*, 48 *Traffic Accident Investigations*, 49 *Radionuclides for Measuring Flow*, 72 *Cracking Up*.

Science Pack for Intermediate GNVQ (1994). Collins Educational, London. Resource pack to cover the mandatory science elements of Intermediate GNVQ Science.

Science, Sprays and Sprayers. AFRC Silsoe. Various articles on spraying, including electrostatic spraying.

Acknowledgements

Grateful acknowledgement is made to the following sources for permission to reproduce material in this unit:

Photographs and figures

Cover photo: Environment Agency; p. 7: Some of the many situations where fluid flow is important: Chiesa della Salute and entrance to the Grand Canal, Venice, Italy, and Grand Canyon, Arizona, USA – J. Allan Cash Ltd; Kerzaz Oasis, Sahara Desert, Algeria – Frans Lemmens/Still Pictures; p. 12: A thermostat – Chris Edwards; p. 13: A thermostatically controlled radiator valve – Chris Edwards; p. 18: A water tower that supplies water to homes – Chris Edwards; p. 23: Michael Faraday – Science & Society Picture Library, Science Museum; p. 34: The Thames at Waterloo Bridge – J. Allan Cash Ltd; p. 37: A waterwheel – Mildrid Cookson; p. 50: An oil pipeline (a section of the Trans Alaska Pipeline near Pump station no. 4) – The British Petroleum Company plc; p. 50: Pipes and meters: A water meter and a gas meter – Chris Edwards; Crop spraying by tractor – Chris Butlin; p. 55: Chladni's figures – University of Edinburgh (Department of Physics and Astronomy), photographer Peter Tuffy, patterns created by Dr Murray M. Campbell; p. 55: Charles Wheatstone and Wheatstone's Alphabet-Dial Telegraph (1858) – Science & Society Picture Library, Science Museum; p. 68: A mercury barometer (Hooke's wheel type barometer) – Science & Society Picture Library, Science Museum; p. 86: Michael Lord – Michael Lord; p. 100: Turbulent flow (Aswan High Dam) – J. Allan Cash Ltd; p. 102: Streamlines in a glacier slowly moving away from Mt Everest – Corbis; p. 114: Boltzmann's tomb – The Open University; p. 120: Osborne Reynolds – The Open University; p. 135: A weir – Chris Edwards; p. 135: Irrigation channels – Holt Studios International; p. 135: Sewage treatment plant – J. Allan Cash Ltd; p. 145: Vortices produced in the cloud downwind of Guadalupe island, Mexico – Corbis; p. 145: Chimney with vortex shedder – Chris Edwards.

Magazine article

Michael Lord, 'The speed of it all', *Electronics Education*, Spring 1994, The Institution of Electrical Engineers.

Other text

The authors and Management Group would also like to thank: The Worshipful Company of Armourers and Brasiers, in association with British ALCAN, who helped finance the development of the liquid flow equipment; The Institute of Physics for the adaptation of 'Investigations of Liquid Flow', written by Chris Butlin while he was the Educational Development Officer at the Institute; British Gas Education for the adaptation of Activities 7, 8, 9 and 10 in 'Laboratory Gas Meter Science Activities for A level', written by Chris Butlin while he was Head of Science at Northfields Upper School, Dunstable; Andrea Butlin for her advice, help and expertise in designing, making and testing prototype equipment.

Index